culture
works

How to **Create Happiness**
in the **Workplace**

··· workbook ···

Kris Boesch

ISBN 978-0-9986711-5-4

First Kalina Publishing softcover edition May 2017

For information about special discounts for bulk purchases, please send requests to cultureworks@choosepeople.com.

If you are interested in having Kris Boesch present at your live event or conference, visit www.krisboesch.com or e-mail kris@choosepeople.com.

Editing and copyediting by Jim Morrison
Cover design by Ivan Kurylenko
Interior design by Toolbox Creative
Illustrations by Alex Seciu

Kalina Publishing Inc.
Denver, CO

"When people feel good about coming to work it ripples into the community, into the homes and the coffee shops and the parks and ball fields. When people are happy at work, they are better parents, spouses, volunteers and citizens. When we make the workplace better, we make the world better."

Kris Boesch

*To all the bosses, leaders, and managers
striving to do the right thing.*

Contents

Chapter 4
Marshal Meaning, Momentum and Money

Chapter 5
Strengthen Shared Identity and Interdependency

Chapter 6
Shift Accountability

Chapter 7
Build Trust and Break Down Divisions

Chapter 8
Nurture Kind, Candid and Constructive Communication

Chapter 9
Repair Relationships

Chapter 10
Create Culture Conducive to Change

How to Use this Workbook

Take action. Make progress. Feel great. Repeat.

If only it were that easy. There were a lot of ideas and recommended steps packed into *Culture Works*. This workbook puts those into bite-size chunks leading you to focused, clear action. In these pages, you'll find ways to apply, implement and integrate the ideas of *Culture Works*. Follow them. You will progress. You will feel great, better than James Brown.

There are several ways you can use this workbook. You can go chapter by chapter, exercise by exercise. You can also choose your own adventure if know where you'd like to start. Maybe there's a hot and heavy initiative on the table you want to tackle first.

Most of the exercises in this book deliver big impact in little time. I know you're busy leaders, managers and supervisors. However, if you find yourself struggling to set aside and honor the short time frames required to make progress, jump straight to Chapter 11 and start there.

Be brave, be bold and be courageous. Take on exercises that make you nervous. Expand your comfort zone! Also do the work of the work. While not always glamorous, it's necessary for the emotional health of your team and the financial health of your organization.

You don't have to do every exercise in every chapter to make progress. However, you do have to commit. You do have to consistently set aside time to think, try on and reflect. Maybe it's an hour a week. Maybe it's a day a month. When's your "culture time?" Schedule this time now (and then keep it sacred.)

If you're serious, you'll get an accountability partner. It could be your entire management team leveraging the deep dive discussion guides each month or simply combining forces with another leader who's looking to step up their culture game. Regardless, what's important is you will learn from one another's experiences—doubling or tripling the knowledge gained from this workbook.

There may be a few exercises that don't make sense for the logistics of your team. Simply adjust them so they do or if that's not possible, scrap 'em. Several exercises recommend referring back to examples in the book so you'll want to have that on hand. Throughout the workbook you will notice several action icons. Here's a legend for this treasure trove of goodness:

✳ Mini-Mantra	⟳ Share
🗑 Obstacle Obliterator	⚑ Checklist
🐾 Bite-Size Step	🚀 Result or Shift
📌 Remember	💡 Takeaway
🕐 Schedule	

One last thought before you begin:

Scoreboards work. They keep us honest. They visually celebrate when we're making headway and restore commitment when we're behind.

Grab a big sticky flipchart piece of paper. Have some markers always accessible. Consider getting the smelly kind if that's your jam. Hang it up in your workspace. If you don't want it super visible, consider tacking it to the back of your office door.

At the top, put something that will make you smile and will remind you that you're focusing on creating an extraordinary workplace culture. Perhaps:

- Make Happy Work

- Our Culture Works

- Secret Sauce

- We've Got This!

Then put numbers 1–15. This workbook has 14 chapters, just like the book. The end of each chapter asks that you share your #1 Takeaway. I'm confident you'll have at least one bonus one. You'll also have several that will simply occur as you do this work. Add in those that come from your partner in crime (aka your accountability partner.)

Send me a picture of your scoreboard and a gift of immeasurable proportions—a token of my HUGE gratitude—will be yours because YOU are, beyond a shadow of a doubt, a stand for joy in the workplace!

Chapter 1

Measure Your Culture's Happiness

- Describe Your Workplace Experience

- Test the Accuracy of Your Litmus Test

- Make the Organizational Triangle Your Own

- Create an Emotionally-Healthy Context

- Lead Your Tromping Elephant Out of the Building

- Remember the Eight Critical Factors

- Checklist, Results and Takeaways

- Deep Dive Discussion

"The measure of my success is the measure of my happiness."

—William John Locke, novelist and playwright

A. Describe Your Workplace Experience

First I want to know, how do you *feel.* Do you feel joy when you walk into your workplace? Why or why not?

_____

_____

_____

What were the results of your assessment? What do you think of those results? Do they seem accurate or not? Why?

_____

_____

_____

As a leader, *your* experience of your workplace is especially contagious. You are a linchpin. Your team reflects your experience.

What are three items you have control over (or could make a request about) to feel more energized, excited and elated at work?

1. _____

2. _____

3. _____

Which of these three will you commit to taking on this month? _____

If you need to schedule time to strategize or to implement, **block out time in your calendar now.**

If it's a mindset shift, **write a short phrase** on sticky notes that will jog your memory. Put these notes where you will see them regularly (the back of your home's bathroom door is surprisingly effective) or change your computer and phone backgrounds to project your phrase. Read it out loud each morning for 19 days.

B. Test the Accuracy of Your Litmus Test

On a scale of 1–10, how do you think your team *feels* about coming to work?

- One is "I would rather get in a car accident than arrive at work. I often tell others how much I hate where I work."

- Ten is "When I wake up in the morning, I really look forward to coming to work. I often tell others how much I love where I work."

Your answer here: _____   Today's date: _____

What top three factors contribute to this number being what it is? Why is it not higher? Why is it not lower?

1. _____

2. _____

3. _____

Now, go ask your team members:

On a scale of 1–10, how do you feel about coming to work? Why? What would make that number one higher?

Name	Number	+One
1.		
2.		
3.		
4.		
5.		
6.		
7.		
8.		

What do you notice? Would you revise your litmus test number? What's one key insight you learned from these exchanges?

_____

_____

_____

(🐾) Name three bite-size steps you can take in the next ten work days to support the "+ One" requests:

1. _____

2. _____

3. _____

(🕐) Schedule implementation time in your calendar now.
Protect this time.

Culture work is strategic important work that often doesn't feel urgent until morale becomes dismal or you lose top talent. It's easy to delay and backburner it. Don't.

C. Make the Organizational Triangle Your Own

Take this paradigm and make it your own. Write your answers to the following:

1. When you consider the financial health of your organization, do you focus on profits, revenue, donations, or grants? If you're a government organization and you don't focus on a financial number, what is the single most important metric you are measured on?

_____

2. What is the common language you use in your organization to describe who you serve? Clients, customers, students, seniors, businesses...

_____

3. What is the common language you use for employees? Employees, team members, advocates, agents, representatives, workers...

_____

4. Draw your Organizational Triangle, using your language listed above. Don't forget the arrows.

5. Name three simple, obvious ways your team takes care of clients that contribute to financial gain or metric success:

○ _____

○ _____

○ _____

Share your organizational triangle with two people on your team. Share how important the team is to sustainable success. Note that while much conversation swirls around customers, ultimately it is the team who is responsible for the success of the organization.

Did you do it? If so, high five! Now, go on to the next exercise.

If not, and you're tempted to go to the next exercise, please pause. The real work of this workbook takes place when you talk and share with others. It's easy to fill out the blanks and "check the box." However, remember, culture is the context within which your team works. When you talk and share with others, you shift the context. You make real deal progress towards creating an extraordinary workplace culture. Keep in mind too that we learn and recall ideas when we teach them to others.

Mini-Mantra: It all starts with our team.

D. Create an Emotionally-Healthy Context

Remember:

- Culture is the context within which your people work.
- Much of this context is defined by the unseen emotional energy flowing through your team.
- Emotions are contagious.
- Emotional intimacy is the social super glue that creates camaraderie and synergy.

What are ten words you would use to describe "the vibe" or the energetic emotional force field you experience when you walk into your organization?

1. _____   6. _____

2. _____   7. _____

3. _____   8. _____

4. _____   9. _____

5. _____   10. _____

 Share with your team:

1. Science shows emotions are contagious.

2. Newton's Cradle shows us that energy—the ability to do work—transfers from one ball to the next.

3. A healthy culture requires that everyone both recognize and own their role in cause and effect, impact and reaction, emotion and motion.

4. Describe how each person is responsible for their emotions, not just for themselves, but for the team as a whole.

5. Briefly ask folks to consider what it feels like when a co-worker shows up with a positive "bring it on" attitude as compared to when they're negative or grumpy.

6. Then ask: What words would you use to describe "the vibe"—the energetic emotional force field—you experience when you walk into our organization?

Put a big check mark here when you've shared with your team: _____. BAM!

 Mini-Mantra: DMV or Disney?

 Obstacle Obliterator: When you consider creating an extraordinary workplace culture, know you're not trying to *make* people happy. You're also not trying to make *everyone* happy. Instead, focus on creating an empowering context within which team members can be happy.

E. Lead Your Tromping Elephant Out of the Building

Of the 25 Elephants on page nine of the book, which resonated most for you as culture challenges on your team? *List first the one that if resolved today would create the most positive impact on your team:*

1. _____

2. _____

3. _____

What three suggestions from the book (or actions you're already aware of) will you commit to taking on in the next 15 business days to make progress on the first elephant on your list?

• _____

• _____

• _____

 Obstacle Obliterator: Give yourself a finish line, a date by when these actions will have been taken.

Date: _____

Tell someone *who you admire* of your commitment. Set up a phone call with them for the day after your finish-line date. Share your follow through and the outcome.

F. Remember the Eight Critical Factors

1. _____. Do your employees have positive perceptions of their supervisor?

2. _____. Do your employees have positive perceptions of their co-workers?

3. _____. Do your employees feel the work they do is meaningful and worthwhile?

4. _____. Are employees satisfied with the level of decision-making authority, control, and freedom they have in their work?

5. _____. Do employees feel their work has an important role in the organization?

6. _____. Do employees feel the organization values, supports, and communicates appropriately with them?

7. _____. Are employees connected to the organization? Is the organization a good match for them?

8. _____. Do employees feel the organization accommodates family needs and encourages a balance between work and family life?

Of these eight, which two are most important to you? How about to those on your team?

Name	Factor	Factor
1.		
2.		
3.		
4.		
5.		
6.		
7.		
8.		

 Remember: Compensation, benefits and perks are not in the top eight factors to having your employees feel good about coming to work.

🏴 Checklist:

Check those exercises and activities you've completed.

A. ____ Describe Your Workplace Experience

B. ____ Test the Accuracy of Your Litmus Test

C. ____ Make the Organizational Triangle Your Own

D. ____ Create an Emotionally-Healthy Context

E. ____ Lead Your Tromping Elephant Out of the Building

F. ____ Remember the Eight Critical Factors

🚀 Results or Shifts

What's one meaningful positive shift, outcome or result you've noticed due to these efforts?

_____

_____

_____

🔄 Now go share your success with someone and celebrate. (I recommend doing a jig.)

💡 Your Top Three Takeaways:

1. _____

2. _____

3. _____

Deep Dive Discussion Guide

Bring your leadership and/or management team together and discuss:

What was your #1 takeaway or insight from Chapter 1?

_____

_____

_____

What did you take on or try on with your team? How did that go? What was harder than you expected? What was easier than you expected?

_____

_____

_____

What's one meaningful positive shift, outcome or result that came out of your efforts? Pause to celebrate! If applicable, what are you going to do to maintain, sustain and continue to nurture that outcome?

_____

_____

_____

What support or help would you like to request from this team? Advice? Best practices? Lessons learned? Being held accountable for following through on a commitment or making a habit stick?

_____

_____

_____

Chapter 2

Know the ROI of Happy Employees

- Define and Improve Your Employment Brand

- Calculate the ROI of Your Culture

- Share the ROI of Happy Employees with Your Biggest Skeptics

- Visualize the Emotional ROI

- Checklist, Results and Takeaways

- Deep Dive Discussion Guide

"The most powerful and enduring brands are built from the heart. They are real and sustainable. Their foundations are stronger because they are built with the strength of the human spirit."

—Howard Schultz, CEO of Starbucks

A. Define and Improve Your Employment Brand

To define your employment brand, answer these questions:

1. What is your reputation in the talent marketplace?

   o What's the word on the street when it comes to working for your organization? Pros? Cons? (You may have to do some research here and ask others.)

   o What did you hear about your organization prior to working for it?

   o What do Glassdoor reviews say about working for your organization?

   _____

   _____

   _____

   _____

2. What work stories do you think former or current employees share with friends? (What work stories do *you* share?)

_____

_____

_____

_____

3. Are you able to attract top talent? Do employees recommend friends for open positions (without being offered incentives)?

_____

_____

_____

_____

4. What one thing about your reputation in the talent marketplace makes you the most proud?

_____

_____

_____

_____

 What's one step you could take in the next month to expand this goodness? (Share stories. Nurture current opportunities to deepen this experience. Speak to it in orientation. Share your pride and highlight it in the "State of the Union.")

_____

Schedule the first bite-size action of this one step now.

5. What's one "X Factor" you wish your organization was known for by potential top talent that it's not known for today?

_____

_____

_____

_____

What's one step you could take in the next month to make this X Factor more of a spoken reality in the daily workplace experience of your employees? This could be as simple as asking your team to share stories about how your organization is X or to brainstorm ideas about how each individual could contribute to making the organization be more X.

_____

Schedule the first bite-size action of this one step now.

Obstacle Obliterator: If the current word on the street is a bit dismal, don't despair. It takes time to turn an employment reputation around. Don't let that stop you. The time to act is right now. The sooner you start, the sooner the grapevine will yield grapes.

If the current word on the street is glowing, first, congrats; second, don't take it for granted. Continue to nurture and nourish the magic.

Mini-Mantra: Water the reputation you want to grow.

B. Calculate the ROI of Your Culture

Calculate your "Ball Park" ROI of the impact of your workplace culture on your bottom line at www.choosepeople.com/culture-calculator. You will need your total number of employees, average salary and your revised litmus test number from the top of page 3 of this workbook.

Number of team members: _____

Average salary: _____

Your (revised) litmus test number: _____

What's your Ball Park number? $ _____

C. Share the ROI of Happy Employees with Your Biggest Skeptics

Put a big bright sticky note on page 16 of your *Culture Works* book and then another one on the ROI stats at the end of the book. Then give it to the person on your team who is most skeptical about this "fluffy rainbows and butterflies culture B.S." Sincerely express, "I thought of you when I read this portion of the book. I know how much you appreciate both financial acumen as well as scientific data. Take a look. Then let's get together so I can hear your thoughts next Tuesday."

D. Visualize the Emotional ROI

Take ten minutes of quiet uninterrupted time.

Read each statement. Close your eyes, take it in, and then spend at least 20 seconds to picture it. (It helps to use your finger or a ruler to keep track of where you are on the list.)

1. Ground your feet.

2. Breathe deep, taking long inhales and exhales.

3. Imagine ripples of energy emanating from your organization.

4. Conjure the image of a household where the parents love their workplace.

5. Imagine their thoughts as they drive home.

6. Think about how they interact with one another.

7. Imagine how they show up to their kids.

8. Imagine their exchange with the neighbors when they get the mail.

9. Now imagine the opposite, a household where the parents hate where they work.

10. Imagine their thoughts as they drive home.

11. Imagine how they show up to one another.

12. Imagine how they show up to their kids.

13. Imagine their exchange with the neighbors when they get the mail.

14. Visualize looking into the eyes of each person on your team.

15. Imagine all of the people they touch once they finish their work day.

16. Watch it reverberate throughout your community.

Write down any interesting thoughts this evoked:

_____

_____

_____

_____

Mini-Mantra: May the force be with you (your team and your community.)

Checklist:

Check those exercises and activities you've completed.

A. _____ Define Your Employment Brand

B. _____ Calculate the ROI of Your Culture

C. _____ Share the ROI of Happy Employees with Your Biggest Skeptics

D. _____ Visualize the Emotional ROI

Results or Shifts

What's one meaningful positive shift, outcome or result you've noticed due to these efforts?

_____

_____

_____

Now, go share your success with someone and celebrate.

Your Top Three Takeaways:

1. _____

2. _____

3. _____

Deep Dive Discussion Guide

Bring your leadership and/or management team together and discuss:

What was your #1 takeaway or insight from Chapter 2?

_____

_____

_____

What did you take on or try on with your team? How did that go? What was harder than you expected? What was easier than you expected?

_____

_____

_____

What's one meaningful positive shift, outcome or result that came out of your efforts? Pause to celebrate! If applicable, what are you going to do to maintain, sustain and continue to nurture that outcome?

_____

_____

_____

What support or help would you like to request from this team? Advice? Best practices? Lessons learned? Being held accountable for following through on a commitment or making a habit stick?

_____

_____

_____

Chapter 3

Fortify Your Foundation

- Author Your Mission
- Dream Your Vision
- Uncover Your Core Values
- Flesh Out Your Values
- Roll Out Your Values
- Checklist, Results and Takeaways
- Deep Dive Discussion Guide

Meaning/ Job Fit

Impact

Organizational Fit

"People don't buy what you do. They buy why you do it."

—Simon Sinek, marketing consultant and author of
Start With Why: How Great Leaders Inspire Everyone to Take Action

As I mentioned in the book, if you love your mission, vision and values and they resonate with your team, skip this chapter and head onwards and upwards. However if they're stale, you can't remember them or they feel "meh," work on.

Author Your Mission

In as few meaningful words as possible, clearly explain how your organization makes the world a better place. Your mission is your purpose. It speaks to WHY you exist. Remember the moving company: "We exist to provide peace of mind, all in one piece." Remember the tractor tire company: "We exist to help nourish and feed our nation."

Connect the dots by asking "Why?" until you get to that **simple elegant nugget that's true**. Stop before it gets too existential or sounds like marketing propaganda.

You will know you have hit the jackpot when your simple phrase gives you goose bumps and resonates with your top performers. It's easy to understand and repeat.

 Remember:

- "Why we work determines how well we work." Lindsay McGregor and Neel Doshi.

- If you're a for-profit company, yes, you exist to make money. But your service or product makes money by bringing joy, solving a problem, providing ease or saving time. This is the work of the company. This is the heart of the company. Without it, there is no money. You wouldn't exist.

- While your mission ideally aligns with your marketing and desired reputation with customers, it is more important for your mission to resonate with your internal team than with your clientele.

Get Started:

1. For context, start by watching Simon Sinek's TED Talk on "How Great Leaders Inspire Action": (https://www.ted.com/talks/simon_sinek_how_great_leaders_inspire_action).

2. To uncover your warm gooey center, consider answering the following questions. Note those words that "pop" the most. When you're done with this exercise, your concise, simple mission statement should consist of a strong verb and simple, tangible language.

What would be lost if our organization ceased to exist?

_____

_____

_____

Why does what we do matter?

_____

_____

_____

How do we contribute to society?

_____

_____

_____

What joy do we bring? And why? Then ask why three more times.

_____

_____

_____

What pain do we solve? And why? Then ask why three more times.

_____

_____

_____

3. Try it on:

We exist to:

_____

We exist to:

_____

We exist to:

_____

We exist to:

_____

We exist to:

_____

Share these ideas with others on your team. What resonates? What doesn't?

_____

_____

_____

4. Sleep on it.

Consider walking your dog while thinking about it. Ponder it in the shower. Contemplate it while cooking.

If you start getting too heady, ask someone who rocks down-to-earth language to rephrase it for you. If you start getting too cliché, ask someone in marketing to help you "pop" a word or two.

5. Try again (and keep trying until it's simple and resonates.)

We exist to:

_____

We exist to:

_____

We exist to:

_____

6. Write your final concise memorable meaningful mission (insert fireworks celebration here!):

_____

B. Dream Your Vision

Your vision provides a single core focus. It is the ruler against which effort, progress and success are measured for the next three years. If you're serious, all of your strategic resources are organized around achieving this effort.

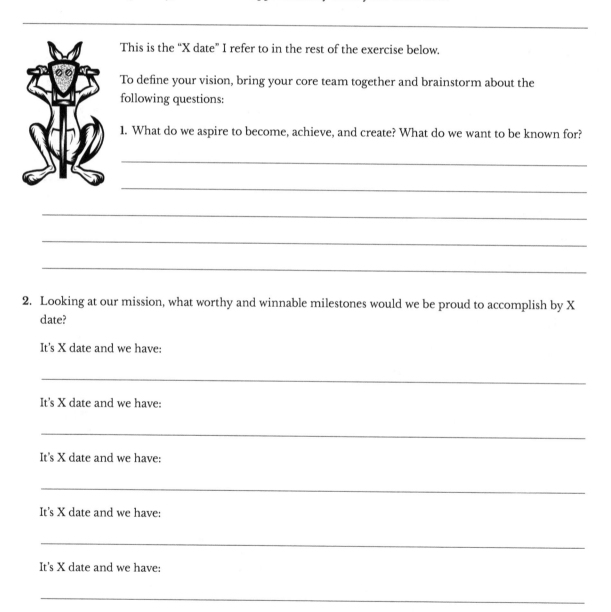

Remember: The biggest challenge with a vision is creating a reachable goal. It has to be worthy and winnable. Nothing is worse than feeling your team's eye rolls of "so what?" or "good luck with that." Make sure to test it by asking—does it inspire us? Does it feel right? Does it sound like BS? Does it feel both possible and challenging?

Start with a meaningful day, date and time approximately three years from now:

_____

This is the "X date" I refer to in the rest of the exercise below.

To define your vision, bring your core team together and brainstorm about the following questions:

1. What do we aspire to become, achieve, and create? What do we want to be known for?

_____

_____

_____

_____

_____

2. Looking at our mission, what worthy and winnable milestones would we be proud to accomplish by X date?

It's X date and we have:

_____

It's X date and we have:

_____

It's X date and we have:

_____

It's X date and we have:

_____

It's X date and we have:

_____

3. Of those listed above, which is most meaningful for fulfilling our mission? What does this milestone make possible?

_____

_____

_____

4. How will you measure success?

_____

_____

_____

Remember: You may be tempted to put a monetary amount in your vision. Or a market share. Or a number of units sold. Don't.

Think through what it would take to get to that number. What's the one result, action or experience that would fulfill your mission and create financial success? Instead of "Within three years, we will dominate our industry," consider, "Within three years, we will solve the number-one customer frustration considered an industry norm."

5. What does the organization look like and feel like if we're achieving this vision?

_____

_____

_____

6. How would we describe the picture of what achieving this vision makes possible for our team and for our clients?

_____

_____

_____

Ready for more fireworks? Write down your final vision goodness.

It's X date and we have:

_____

We will measure this by:

_____

 Share with your entire team the three-year vision and describe what it makes possible.

C. Uncover Your Core Values

Your values set the bar for how you and your team are going to work together. They guide your decisions and thus your words, behaviors and actions. The daily experience of how you choose to fulfill the mission and reach the vision is rooted in your values. When followed, your values create your desired reputation.

1. To uncover your values, first answer the following:

    What do we stand for? What do we stand against?

    _____

    _____

    _____

    What values guide our decisions when making tough choices?

    _____

    _____

    _____

    What are we known for? What is our "way"?

    _____

    _____

    _____

    What values are highlighted in shared stories? What are our common phrases, ethos, behaviors and attitudes?

    _____

    _____

    _____

2. In a different color pen, circle up to 15 value words or phrases in your responses above.

3. Determine whose input you would like regarding the values (leadership, management, top talent, great culture-fit representatives.) Ask each individual to choose their top three from the list of 15. This should narrow down the list significantly.

    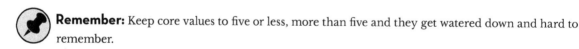 **Remember:** Keep core values to five or less, more than five and they get watered down and hard to remember.

4. Then discuss the tallied results. Ask voters to speak to the "why" behind their selections. **Listen carefully. This dialogue will be rich with phrases that may be even better than the original values suggested.** Make sure to visibly capture these. Once all the "whys" are on the table, push the team to narrow down to the core.

    Often you'll find a single value represents several other nuanced values. Conveniently, these nuances can be incorporated in this next exercise.

D. Flesh Out Your Values

What does each value look like in practice? Describe what it looks like for a team member to embody that value. What attitudes and behaviors could you evaluate that align with this value? Try to start each bullet with an active verb. (See the example on page 32 of the *Culture Works* book.)

Value #1 _____

- _____
- _____
- _____

Value #2 _____

- _____
- _____
- _____

Value #3 _____

- _____
- _____
- _____

Value #4 _____

- _____
- _____
- _____

Value #5 _____

- _____
- _____
- _____

E. Roll Out Your Values

 Once you have these pretty well-defined, roll out the values (with the action describers for each) to the entire staff as a *rough draft*. It's important that the team has an opportunity to contribute their 66 cents. Don't ask for generic feedback. Specifically ask:

- Do these values resonate?
- Is there a value that feels like it's "missing" and is more important than those listed?
- What do you think of the expectations about how these values would be "lived" in our organization?

Again, listen carefully. Make sure the team feels heard. Incorporate their feedback and finalize the values. This should be done quickly, don't let this get put on the backburner!

Checklist:

Check those action items you've completed.

A. _____ Author Your Mission

B. _____ Dream Your Vision

C. _____ Uncover Your Core Values

D. _____ Flesh Out Your Values

E. _____ Roll Out Your Values

Results or Shifts

What's one meaningful positive shift, outcome or result you've noticed due to these efforts?

_____

_____

_____

Now go share your success with someone and celebrate.

Your Top Three Takeaways:

1. _____

2. _____

3. _____

Deep Dive Discussion Guide

Bring your leadership and/or management team together and discuss:

What was your #1 takeaway or insight from Chapter 3?

_____

_____

_____

What did you take on or try on with your team? How did that go? What was harder than you expected? What was easier than you expected?

_____

_____

_____

What's one meaningful positive shift, outcome or result that came out of your efforts? Pause to celebrate! If applicable, what are you going to do to maintain, sustain and continue to nurture that outcome?

_____

_____

_____

What support or help would you like to request from this team? Advice? Best practices? Lessons learned? Being held accountable for following through on a commitment or making a habit stick?

_____

_____

_____

Chapter 4

Marshal Meaning, Momentum and Money

- Evaluate Your Current Heartbeat

- Operationalize Your Mission, Vision and Values

- Create and Implement a Strategic Plan

- Marry Money to the Mission

- Show Them the Money

- Checklist, Results and Takeaways

- Deep Dive Discussion Guide

Meaning/ Job Fit **Autonomy** **Impact** **Organizational Fit**

"If you want to build a ship, don't herd people together to collect wood and don't assign them tasks and work, but rather teach them to long for the endless immensity of the sea."

—Antoine de Saint-Exupery, writer and poet

A. Evaluate Your Current Heartbeat

1. *Without looking at them...*write your mission, vision and values here:

Mission:

_____

Vision:

_____

Values:

_____

You can look now. How'd you do?

_____

2. Now go ask five of your front-line staff if they can tell you what the mission, vision and values are. How'd it go?

_____ Alive and kicking. They rocked it, down to every word. BAM!

_____ Definitely a pulse. They got some pieces and couldn't remember others.

_____ Dead on arrival. They mocked me a bit and chuckled "Uh, say what?"

B. Operationalize Your Mission, Vision and Values

In what ways do you currently incorporate your mission, vision and values into the workplace experience of your employees?

_____

_____

_____

Looking at pages 30 and 31 of the book, which three areas of the Employment Cycle and Organizational Processes could most benefit from integration with your values? Hint: It's often where there's the biggest disconnect between the values and the current experience. Of these three, circle the one in which integration would be the most impactful.

1. _____

2. _____

3. _____

What are two bite-size steps you can take in the next 15 business days to either deepen what's working or integrate your values into the process you circled above? Consider the ideas outlined on pages 32–35 of the *Culture Works* book.

1. _____

2. _____

 Block out time in your schedule to complete these now.

C. Create and Implement a Strategic Plan

Step 1: Set aside 75 minutes of dedicated time to think through these strategic questions and write down your thoughts.

Evaluate the Past

1. What were our accomplishments this last year?

2. Did we celebrate them?

3. What mistakes did we make this last year?

4. Did we evaluate them, learn from them and implement new systems or processes to address them?

_____

_____

_____

_____

_____

Evaluate the Present

1. Right now, what's working?

2. Can we expand or leverage what's working?

3. Right now, what's not working?

4. Of these, what is mission critical to address?

5. What do we need to do next year about mission critical concerns?

6. What are our key actions, activities, products, services, or projects that we need to keep at the forefront?

7. Is there anything we need to do differently to make sure these core pieces continue to be nurtured as priorities?

_____

_____

_____

_____

_____

Evaluate Opportunities:

1. What projects do we currently have under construction?

2. How strapped are we right now from a resource perspective (time/energy/money)?

3. What's needed to advance our mission and realize our vision?

4. Brainstorm strategic opportunities for the organization and for various departments.

5. Of these, which three would you prioritize? Why?

6. Are any of these as important or more important than current commitments?

_____

_____

_____

_____

_____

Step 2: Schedule a half-day with your leadership team. In preparation ask them to ponder the same questions above. They should also gather input and thoughts on these questions from their teams. In this half-day, simply listen, capture and clarify the input on the past, present and future opportunities.

Step 3: Set aside two more half days. Download from www.gazelles.com their wonderful, free **Gazelles One-Page Strategic Plan and its accompanying instructions.** Spend one half day working through the big picture strategy portion and one half day working on the implementation portion.

Step 4: Share the strategic plan with the entire team. Speak to the following:

- Our successes, struggles and learnings from last year.

- The strategies and initiatives that were considered for this upcoming year.

- Why these goals were chosen for the final plan and why the others were not.

- Whether all the goals are equally important and the prioritization of the goals.

- How the goals support fulfilling your mission.

- How the goals move the organization closer to achieving the vision.

Prepare your talking points here:

_____

_____

_____

_____

_____

_____

_____

_____

_____

_____

Step 5: Give each employee a copy of the almost completed Gazelles One-Page Strategic Plan. Then have each manager meet one-on-one with their team members defining individual work priorities and lead indicator goals for the quarter (rather than lag results.) Set a short finish line for these to be completed.

 Schedule your one-on-ones now.

Step 6: Implement a "Cadence of Accountability" from *The Four Disciplines of Execution* **by Chris McChesney, Sean Covey and Jim Huling.** Each week, have a quick stand up meeting. In that meeting, have each individual briefly speak to:

- The one to three strategic bite-size tasks they will accomplish that week towards their quarterly performance priorities.

- The following week, have each individual speak to their success in accomplishing those tasks (high five!) or not (help needed?)

- The strategic tasks they are taking on for the upcoming week.

 Determine the best day and time of the week for the team and schedule it now indefinitely. Hold this time sacred and short. No scope creep.

Step 7: Measure progress, celebrate success and describe the future monthly. At the end of each month take 40 minutes with your team and write down your successes. Then make sure to measure how far the team has progressed towards the quarterly and annual goals.

Obstacle Obliterator: You don't have to wait until your strategic plan is complete. Start celebrating now.

Successes for the month of _____:

- _____
- _____
- _____
- _____
- _____
- _____
- _____
- _____
- _____
- _____

Then forward vision what will be accomplished at the end of the upcoming month. "It's October 31st and we have beta tested the new software; we've hired two new developers; we've resolved the bug on the current software, and we won the Halloween contest."

Forward Vision for Next Month:

It's _____ and we have...(choose three performance goals plus one fun goal.)

- _____
- _____
- _____
- _____

Step 8: Revisit the map and goals quarterly. When it comes to goals, don't just set it and forget it. Stay focused. Follow up. Adjust. Schedule this time into your calendar now.

 Mini-Mantra: Plan the strategic work, work the strategic plan.

D. Marry Money to the Mission

Talk about why money matters. Connect the money to the mission, the purpose to the profit.

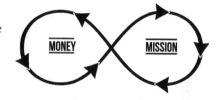

 Schedule this topic on the agenda for your next all hands meeting.

Start by drawing a picture of an infinity symbol. Write money on one side and mission on the other (like the picture above.)

 Share with your team how:

- Your organization does not exist to make money. It exists to fulfill your mission.

- Money is energy resulting from successfully fulfilling your mission.

- The mission is anemic and powerless without money.

- Money and mission are married. They depend on and feed one another.

- As the mission expands, so does the money. As the money expands, so does the mission.

- The energy literally swirls down, up and around from one side of the infinity symbol continuum to the other.

- Give specific examples based on your organization's model and mission.

Big money equals big impact. Big impact equals big money.

This simple shift creates an empowering cultural context for your team. Once your meaningful mission is nailed down, this is low hanging fruit.

E. Show Them the Money

 Use the $100 Tool to share how your organization makes, saves and spends money in a tangible, accurate way.

1. Get 100 one dollar bills.

2. On a flip chart or white board, break down by percentage your high-level income streams. Then break down by percentage your high-level expenses.

3. Gather your team and speak about how your organization makes, saves and spends money. Share which verticals, products and services are the most and least profitable. Explain why you choose to keep those that are less profitable—loss leader, bread and butter, competitive edge.

4. Then talk through expenses. As you detail each expense, hand out the dollar bills equivalent to the expense percentage (10 percent = 10 dollars) to an individual employee, picking a new employee for each expense.

5. Speak about employee payroll, payroll taxes, workers compensation and benefits last.

6. Then show them, with the dollars left in your hand, the profit. Explain how this is taxed, leaving a net profit and how that money has to be used to pay off debt as well as to reinvest in the organization to create financial sustainability or to spur growth. Explain how it is this money—the money that's left over—that funds raises, better benefits, new uniforms, additional staff, or new equipment.

7. Help them understand which numbers they can impact and which ones they can't. You want them to leave knowing how they can individually help the organization make and save money.

8. Depending on your team, it can also be valuable to explain the difference between profit and cash flow. You may want to share the role of revenue to profit.

How'd it go? What did your team ask? What did they share? Based on their response, is there anything you would want to make sure to include next time you share the $100 Tool? (I recommend using it annually. Put it on the calendar. It could be a company holiday.)

_____

_____

_____

_____

🏴 Checklist:

Check those action items you've completed.

A. _____ Evaluate Your Current Heartbeat

B. _____ Two Steps to Operationalize Your Mission, Vision and Values

C. Create and Implement a Strategic Plan:

_____ Step 1—Your thoughts on the past, present and future

_____ Step 2—Capturing your leadership team's input and feedback

_____ Step 3—Completion of the Gazelles One-Page Strategic Plan

_____ Step 4—Sharing the Gazellea One-Page Strategic Plan with your team

_____ Step 5—Identifying quarterly goals for each person on your team

_____ Step 6—Implement a weekly "Cadence of Accountability"

_____ Step 7—Measure progress, celebrate success and describe the future

_____ Step 8—Schedule to revisit quarterly

D. _____ Marry Money to the Mission

E. _____ Show Them the Money ($100 Tool)

🚀 Results or Shifts

What's one meaningful positive shift, outcome or result you've noticed due to these efforts?

_____

_____

_____

_____

🔄 Now go share your success with someone and celebrate.

💡 Your Top Three Takeaways:

1. _____

2. _____

3. _____

Deep Dive Discussion Guide

Bring your leadership and/or management team together and discuss:

What was your #1 takeaway or insight from Chapter 4?

_____

_____

_____

What did you take on or try on with your team? How did that go? What was harder than you expected? What was easier than you expected?

_____

_____

_____

What's one meaningful positive shift, outcome or result that came out of your efforts? Pause to celebrate! If applicable, what are you going to do to maintain, sustain and continue to nurture that outcome?

_____

_____

_____

What support or help would you like to request from this team? Advice? Best practices? Lessons learned? Being held accountable for following through on a commitment or making a habit stick?

_____

_____

_____

Chapter 5

Strengthen Shared Identity and Interdependency

- Instill Tribe Trifecta

- Bolster Known, Matter and Included

- Illustrate and Ground Interdependency Awareness

- Reinforce Common Ground

- Discuss—What's Your Shared Identity Look Like?

- Instill the Row Boat Analogy

- Shift Towards Family Spirit

- Practice Meaningful Appreciation and Recognition

- Optional: Create Formalized Peer-to-Peer Recognition

- Optional: Pump Up Camaraderie

- Checklist, Results and Takeaways

- Deep Dive Discussion Guide

| Supervisor | Co-workers | Meaning/Job Fit | Impact | Organizational Fit |

"When we try to pick out anything by itself, we find it hitched to everything else in the Universe."

—John Muir, naturalist and philosopher

Many of the exercises in this section focus on creating an emotionally healthy workplace context for your team.

A. Instill Tribe Trifecta—Organization, Team, Individual

Your organization is a conscious community brought together to fulfill a shared purpose.

This purpose is at the core of your team's shared identity. Every time there's alignment between what's best for the individual, what's best for the team and what's best for the organization, this shared identity is reinforced.

Work through these questions to find opportunities to instill tribe trifecta.

Does loyalty and commitment to what's best for the organization supersede team and individual agendas? Write down examples of when departments yielded to the organization and individuals yielded to the team.

_____

_____

_____

_____

_____

_____

Remember: In order for individuals to put the organization first, you must consistently demonstrate the organization has the best interest of its team members in mind.

How does your organization demonstrate consideration of team members? Some examples: training, an unexpected bonus, firing toxic employees, real cream for coffee, and soft toilet paper in the bathroom.

_____

_____

_____

When has your team banded together for the greater good? (Usually during a time of struggle and resulting in collective courage.)

_____

_____

_____

Share these stories of collective courage often. They are part of your organization's heritage and legacy. Insert them into orientation, in meetings where appropriate and in "State of the Union" messages. Make sure to collect these stories in your organizational canon. Don't let them fall into the forgotten.

 Go share one of these stories with a new employee this week.

Do you have a department or individual who is consistently self-focused rather than team-focused?

_____

_____

_____

Have you or other leaders or managers provided *unwarranted* preferential treatment to a single employee or department? If so, why? Is this in alignment with your values? If not, did this get corrected and addressed?

_____

_____

_____

Remember: When an organization puts an individual first, it undermines the foundational bond of "we're all in this together." The result is morale mutiny.

Are you currently stuck focusing on the challenge of one employee? If so, answer the following:

1. What's best for the success of the organization?

2. For the team?

3. For the individual?

4. Can we simultaneously accomplish all three *without* tying ourselves in knots?

5. If not, what are the facts of the misalignment?

_____

_____

_____

_____

_____

Having worked through the above questions, what are two tangible bite-size steps you can take in the next 10 business days to increase a sense of alignment between the organization, the team and individual employees?

1. _____

2. _____

Block out time for these in your schedule now.

B. Bolster Known, Matter & Included

At the core of the reciprocal, symbiotic beauty of an extraordinary workplace culture is the individual need to be known, to matter and to be included. When these needs are met, you've laid the foundation to fulfill the organization's needs. One feeds the other. They are interdependent.

First, make a short list of the team members you're closest to as well as a short list of those with whom you're least connected.

Closest   Least Connected

_____   _____

_____   _____

_____   _____

_____   _____

What do you notice when looking at these two lists? Is there a pattern? Does that pattern require your attention and increased awareness?

_____

_____

Work through these questions to uncover how your team feels about being known, matter and included.

Do the individuals on your team **feel known?** Consider *each* team member. Would you say they feel:

1. Thought of, remembered, considered? (As compared to invisible, ignored or forgotten.)

2. You and the team know their goofy quirks, pet's name and a few personal details about their likes and dislikes?

3. You know when they're in a good space and when they're struggling?

4. They are missed when absent?

_____

_____

_____

_____

Do the individuals on your team **feel their contribution matters?** Consider *each* team member. Would you say they feel:

1. If they go the extra mile, you or the team notices and appreciates their efforts?

2. If they slack, do you or your team team notice and reach out to inquire and support?

3. If they make a mistake, it matters?

4. The results of their work are important to the success of the team and the organization?

_____

_____

_____

_____

Do the individuals on your team **feel included?** Consider *each* team member. Would you say they feel:

1. A sense of belonging? Part of the tribe?

2. Their presence is desired by the team?

3. They know the fight song, unwritten rules and inside jokes?

4. Their contribution is made more meaningful by being part of the team?

_____

_____

_____

_____

 On these last three questions, test your answers. Take 15 minutes with each team member to ask how they feel when it comes to being known, feeling they matter and are included. Do not let this exchange slip into the realm of projects, performance, updates etc.

What did you learn?

_____

_____

_____

C. Discuss, Illustrate and Ground Interdependency Awareness

For interdependency awareness to be present, each person on your team needs to understand both the importance of their role and the role of their co-workers in fulfilling the mission.

 Remember: The Mouse Trap game, the silver ball is the sexiest piece in the box and completely useless without the other parts.

Do you have departments that are either silo'd, competitive or don't appreciate work done by other departments? Do you have individuals who think "I'm all good" because they've reached individual performance goals?

_____

_____

 Obstacle Obliterator: This next exercise dissipates the disconnect causing these challenges. Even if you don't have these struggles, complete this exercise. It will inoculate you.

Interdependency Awareness Team Glue:

1. Schedule 30 minutes with your team.

2. When your team gathers, prep them for the next step by asking them to look for lessons and insights regarding teamwork.

3. Together watch the three-minute OK GO music video of the song "This Too Shall Pass" on YouTube. Make sure it's the Rube Goldberg version.

4. Ask your team to speak to the factors that made this teamwork successful. For facilitation, popcorn it or round robin, whichever works better for your team. Use a flipchart or a visual shared board to capture everyone's contributions.

5. After hearing from the team, make sure these insights were covered:

   o Each piece is mission critical to the whole. No one piece can say, "I don't feel like showing up today."

- The whole is mission critical to each piece. Each piece is inconsequential without the rest of the system.

- Each piece is impacted by the piece before it and impacts the piece after it.

- A clear vision of the shared purpose.

- The importance of collaboration, communication and coordination.

- The importance of commitment, perseverance and grit.

- Rhythm and cadence shifts as needed.

- There's easy forgiveness and learning from mistakes—paint on the band and multiple broken TVs.

- Lots of planning, trying on and tweaking. You are committed to continuous improvement.

- The importance of the "back of the house" to the "front of the house." While four people are in the spotlight, it took the entire crew to make it successful.

Then talk through your organization's cycle of work.

If just your team is attending, have each person take a couple of minutes to speak about their role and their top two challenges in making sure to do "their part" well.

If the whole organization is attending, have each department speak to their role and their challenges. Have each department kindly and candidly make three requests regarding what they need from other departments to be more successful.

 Mini-Mantra: Each piece is mission critical to the whole and the whole is mission critical to each piece.

D. Reinforce Common Ground

 Obstacle Obliterator: Whenever disunity begins to take hold of your team, head to common ground.

 At the heart of divisiveness is separateness, me vs. you, us vs. them. Bring those who are committed to their differences together and remind them how much they have in common. They both want to:

- Support themselves and/or their families.

- Contribute.

- Be part of something that's meaningful and bigger than themselves.

- Do work that makes them proud.

- Work for an organization that makes them proud.

- Be acknowledged and appreciated for a job well done.

- Be better tomorrow than they are today.

- Have someone who will champion their potential and who believes in them.

- Work well with and enjoy their co-workers.

Remind them of the magical serendipity—destiny if you will—that all of their circumstances, experiences and choices brought them to this place, to this time, to work with this team.

 Mini-Mantra: We're all on the same team, wearing the same jersey.

E. Discuss—What's Your Shared Identity Look Like?

Gather your team for 20 minutes and consider together, what would a tattoo of your organization's logo say about the person sporting it? How would it communicate their personality, reputation and identity?

This tattoo question helps put concrete thinking around what can feel like an elusive concept.

To help this dialogue:

- Share the Harley Davidson example from page 51 in *Culture Works* book.

- Look to your mission, vision and values.

- Ask:

    o If you were to add to your logo a few embellishments, would a heart with Mom in the middle be appropriate? Or would skulls, four leaf clovers, or tribal markings be more accurate?

    o What's your common language, team colors, secret handshake, or fight song?

    o Who gets to be a member of your tribe? Who doesn't?

    o What do you stand for? What do you stand against?

    o What are your principles for working together?

 Schedule this discussion now.

F. Instill the Row Boat Analogy

To cultivate the experience of being crew, rather than passengers, take 15 minutes with your team and walk through this analogy:

- Imagine we're all in a rowboat.

- All of us are rowing with fervor, in rhythm, in the right direction. Heck, we're even singing in unison our organization's fight song.

- In this moment, we are crew, not passengers.

- There is a sense of glee in our collective hard work. Our shared commitment. We can feel the sun on our faces and the ocean spray salt on our lips. The blisters on our hands, while uncomfortable, feel worth it.

- This is the experience I want for us every day.

What we need to be conscientious and cautious of:

- The temptation to just ride along, not carrying our weight.

- Rowing really hard with good intentions, but in the wrong direction.

- Throwing down an anchor in frustration.

- Poking holes in our boat by being careless.

- Engaging in a paddle battle.

- Hitting one another with our oars.

- Being aloof to those who are new in learning the rhythm.

 Schedule sharing this analogy now.

Mini-Mantra: We're crew, not passengers.

G. Shift Towards Family Spirit

Obstacle Obliterator: When organizations pride themselves on being "like a family," they often have familial dysfunctions. There's usually codependency, enabled bad behavior, a sense of sibling rivalry and a lack of accountability.

Yet most of us value real deal, authentic connection with those in our daily sphere. When we say we're like a family, we're saying we want the positive experience of family. We want family spirit. This slight distinction is key.

Instead of saying, "we're a family" or "we're like a family," try on "we have family spirit" and consider Zappos definition, *"We watch out for each other, care for each other, and go above and beyond for each other because we believe in each other and we trust each other."*

Remember: In most cases, the reality is your employees are not your family. There's no promise to love or employ your employees unconditionally. You pay for performance. People are not entitled to employment. You are not entitled to their work. At the end of the day there is an employment agreement that binds your relationship, not blood.

H. Practice Meaningful Recognition and Appreciation

Appreciation is noticing, acknowledging and giving testimony when your employees go above and beyond. Appreciation affirms that an individual's contribution matters. You witness their effort and value their contribution.

Where are you on the appreciation spectrum? For some managers, appreciation is so rare teams wonder if anyone notices their work. On the other end, managers who say "thank you" too often can appear inauthentic.

_____

_____

List three people on your team who have recently:

• Exceeded expectations.

• Taken on a challenge or learned a new skill.

• Completed a milestone on a difficult project.

• Taken the initiative to improve a process or resolve a problem.

1. _____

2. _____

3. _____

With these three individuals:

1. Reach out to them to express your gratitude face to face. If this venue is not available, give them a call.

2. Speak to what they did specifically.

3. Say what their effort means to you and to the success of the larger goals.

4. Talk up. Share their accomplishment with someone outside of your immediate team or above you and ask them to circle back and acknowledge this team member.

 Reach out to these individuals this week (the sooner, the better.)

 Block 30 minutes each week into your schedule—15 minutes to evaluate if someone in your organization has done something worth acknowledging and 15 minutes to reach out to them.

 Remember:

- Don't praise average work.

- Don't praise to motivate someone.

- Don't praise in public unless you're looking to shift behaviors.

- Don't do employee of the month.

- You don't need to write a thank-you note.

- You don't need a reward to go with your appreciation.

These next two exercises are optional. While they are nice to have, they are not mission critical. The other exercises in this chapter should be prioritized.

I. Optional: Create Formalized Peer-to-Peer Recognition

Whether considering Rock Star Cards or following REI's example (pages 58 and 59 of the *Culture Works* book), how could you create a meaningful formalized peer-to-peer recognition program for your team?

_____

_____

_____

_____

J. Optional: Pump Up Camaraderie

The Ice Bucket Challenge was brilliant. It's an idea worth trying to leverage. What kind of Ice Bucket Challenge could you launch for your team (page 50 of the *Culture Works* book)? Create and test your idea with these criteria. Would participants feel they are:

- Contributing to something bigger than themselves?

- Part of a tribe with a shared commitment and enjoy a sense of "we're all in this together"?

- Members of a caring team?

- Valued—where their contribution is witnessed by the team?
- Having fun and contributing to shared joy?
- Voluntarily choosing to participate and inviting others to do the same, or supporting others in their commitment? (No forced fun.)

 Checklist:

Check those action items you've completed.

A. _____ Instill Tribe Trifecta

B. _____ Bolster Known, Matter and Included

C. _____ Illustrate and Ground Interdependency Awareness

D. _____ Reinforce Common Ground

E. _____ Discuss—What's Your Shared Identity Look Like?

F. _____ Instill the Row Boat Analogy

G. _____ Shift Towards Family Spirit

H. _____ Practice Meaningful Appreciation and Recognition

I. _____ **Optional:** Create Formalized Peer-to-Peer Recognition

J. _____ **Optional:** Pump Up Camaraderie

Results or Shifts

What's one meaningful positive shift, outcome or result you've noticed due to these efforts?

_____

_____

_____

Now go share your success with someone and celebrate.

Your Top Three Takeaways:

1. _____

2. _____

3. _____

Deep Dive Discussion Guide

Bring your leadership and/or management team together and discuss:

What was your #1 takeaway or insight from Chapter 5?

_____

_____

_____

What did you take on or try on with your team? How did that go? What was harder than you expected? What was easier than you expected?

_____

_____

_____

What's one meaningful positive shift, outcome or result that came out of your efforts? Pause to celebrate! If applicable, what are you going to do to maintain, sustain and continue to nurture that outcome?

_____

_____

_____

What support or help would you like to request from this team? Advice? Best practices? Lessons learned? Being held accountable for following through on a commitment or making a habit stick?

_____

_____

_____

Chapter 6

Shift Accountability

- Shift from Shame to Support
- Apply the Workable Integrity Checklist
- Sip Truth Serum
- Clarify Character and Competency Expectations
- Teach Your Team the Peer Accountability Imperative
- Explain How to Change
- Know When to Stop Investing in an Employee
- Define Your Deal Breakers
- Checklist, Results and Takeaways
- Deep Dive Discussion Guide

Supervisor

Co-workers

Impact

Organizational Support

Organizational Fit

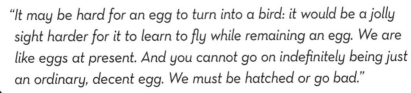

"It may be hard for an egg to turn into a bird: it would be a jolly sight harder for it to learn to fly while remaining an egg. We are like eggs at present. And you cannot go on indefinitely being just an ordinary, decent egg. We must be hatched or go bad."

—C.S. Lewis, novelist and poet

Accountability is key to an extraordinary workplace culture. Holding people accountable means witnessing both when someone is being successful and when they are struggling. When you see success, follow up with meaningful appreciation and recognition as outlined in the last chapter. When you see struggle, check in to see how you can support, coach or guide.

A. Shift from Shame to Support

 Shift your team's thinking about accountability from "place blame for wrongdoing" to the "ability to count." What does that mean? It means having your team members feel that their efforts make a difference and an impact. For an individual's work to be impactful, the work has to be done well. If everyone on the team is committed to one another's success, as well as to the team's success, standing by and saying nothing as a co-worker slips, flails, or drowns wouldn't be an option. Team members would step in and find out how they can help.

Remember: If someone isn't pulling their weight or isn't being kind and there's no reaction, things get wonky fast. As a leader, when you say nothing, you implicitly give permission, perpetuating bad behaviors. Subpar behavior or performance becomes normal, accepted. A new low standard is set. Identity is questioned and pride is lost.

Mini-Mantra: Accountability is a question of workability, not morality.

B. Apply the Workable Integrity Check List

Who is someone on your team who is struggling?

_____

Walk through each item on the Workable Integrity Checklist below. Where is the main disconnect for members of your team? Then help those individuals figure out how to address or repair it.

Inspired by the work of Werner Erhard and the article "Integrity: A Positive Model that Incorporates the Normative Phenomena of Morality, Ethics, and Legality," by Werner H. Erhard, Michael C. Jensen, and Steve Zaffron (unpublished paper at http://ssrn.com/abstract=920265; copyright 2005–2009 Werner Erhard, Michael C. Jensen, Steve Zaffron).

The Workable Integrity Checklist:

☐ Nothing hidden.
☐ Being truthful and honest.
☐ Working from an empowering context.
☐ Doing well what you do.
☐ Doing the work as it was meant to be done or better without cutting corners.
☐ Honoring your word.
☐ Doing what you know to do.
☐ Doing what you said on time.
☐ Doing what others expect you to do even if you haven't said you would do it.
☐ Speaking up immediately when you realize you won't be doing this as expected or won't be doing it at all.

Remember: Empowering context refers to actively choosing and taking on a task, enjoyable or not, because you know the value and impact it brings to the work. If you are aware someone has expectations of you, unless you negotiate changes, you are responsible for meeting them.

C. Sip Truth Serum

Can you name a promise or commitment you've been making to the team and never fulfilled?

_____

If the truth is you're not going to fulfill that promise, no matter how good your intentions, talk to your team and sip some truth serum now.

Continuous lack of integrity chips away at your credibility. Clay feet become quicksand. Have the humility to pivot when needed. Be less committed to looking good. Swallow some still warm crow and wash it down with truth serum.

 Or, if you're still committed, you have to fulfill your promise in the next 30 days. Mark a big RED finish line X in your calendar now.

If that's not possible, sip. If another month goes by and you haven't fulfilled your promise, your credibility will suffer another blow. That warm crow becomes cold and congealed.

D. Clarify Character and Competency Expectations

 Remember: High expectations lead to high performance.

What does it take to be a member of your team?

On the character side:

- What attitudes and behaviors are expected?
- What values and principles for working together need to be practiced?

_____

_____

_____

_____

On the competency side:

- What skills and expertise are needed to be successful in each position?
- What does excellence look like? What does subpar performance look like?

Position #1: _____

_____

_____

Position #2 _____

_____

_____

Position #3 _____

_____

_____

On a scale of zero to three evaluate each team member for character and competency:

Exemplary—3, Meets Expectations—2, Needs Improvement—1, Unacceptable—0

Name	Character	Competency
1.		
2.		
3.		
4.		
5.		
6.		
7.		
8.		

What do you notice? Do you have someone whose character is delightful but whose competence is subpar? How can you support them in improving their skills? Or do you have someone whose competence is amazing and their character is annoying or dreadful? How can you support them in shifting their attitude or behavior? Do you have someone who excels at both? Go acknowledge them. Do you have someone who struggles with both? Start the process to set them free.

_____

_____

_____

 What are three bite-size steps you will take in the next 10 business days to activate your character and competency expectations? How will you support team members in reaching those expectations?

1. _____

2. _____

3. _____

 Schedule these in your calendar now.

E. Teach Your Team the Peer Accountability Imperative

If your team struggles to hold one another accountable, avoids confrontation or kvetches to co-workers about their frustrations with other team members, this is the *first* of several dialogues to have with your team. (More to come in Chapter 8.)

 Schedule 30 minutes with your team.

 First, comunicate your expectations.

- Speak to the importance of both character and competency.

- Share that one of your character expectations is to kindly, candidly and constructively communicate concerns directly to one another.

- Explain triangulation and why it must stop. Triangulation creates gossip. Gossip is not tolerated.

- Caution your team about the "sneaky sounding boards" on page 101 of the *Culture Works* book.

- Let them know if they come to you about another team member, you will always ask if they have spoken to the other team member directly first. If they haven't, in most cases, you will ask them to do so. You'll check in to see how it went.

- Another expectation is for each team member to receive with graciousness a co-worker's courageous willingness to bring up a concern.

Then rhetorically ask: Have you ever failed to hold a co-worker accountable because you wanted to be nice and didn't want to hurt their feelings?

Be empathetic: Welcome to the world of humanity. We like to be liked. The fear of being disliked is at the root of why peer accountability is rare.

Then ask: In an instance where your co-worker delivered subpar performance:

- Did you go ahead and do the work yourself, making assumptions about why your co-worker didn't complete it?

- Did you then feel resentful?

- Did you then make comments about that person's inability to do their work to your spouse, co-workers, or supervisor?

Or perhaps, if it had to do with character or attitude:

- Did you avoid your co-worker?

- Did you make comments about that person to your spouse, co-workers or supervisor?

If you did, *consider your co-worker never had the chance to correct their behavior because you didn't speak up.* **And** if you spoke to others, you started destructive gossip.

Be empathetic: We've all been there. We have avoided, couched, lied, placated, agreed and then turned around and told someone else what we really think, seeking validation for our feelings—all in the name of not wanting to hurt someone's feelings.

Require: As a team, we must renounce unkind niceness. We must be a stand for one another's success.

Then share: We often think people won't like us if we hold them accountable. Yet, we all have stories of someone who was brave enough to bring a blind spot to our attention, an act that changed how we acted, leading us to success, self-actualization or richer relationships.

When you're truly committed to someone else's success, you hold them accountable. Holding someone accountable tells them you value their contribution and that their work makes a difference. If they don't do their work, or don't do it well, it matters. They matter.

Help your co-worker be the best they can be by communicating when something is amiss. To not say anything is to sit quietly by and watch as their reputation deteriorates. When done with the intent to support someone in their success, reaching out to your fellow team member and making them aware of a blind spot is the real kindness.

Ask: What do you think of what I just shared? Can we all commit to being a stand for one another's success and communicating our concerns directly?

 Mini-Mantra: Renounce unkind niceness.

Mini-Mantra: Be a stand for one another's success.

 Mini-Mantra: No death by triangulation.

F. Explain How to Change

Obstacle Obliterator: Ever notice how when you meet with an employee about a concern, they agree, apologize and then nothing changes? Chances are you only shared **what** needs to change, not **how** to change it.

Name someone on your team who is struggling and their specific challenge. Then name three tangible action items they could take to improve the character or competency.

Name: _____

Challenge: _____

Three tangible actions items: (learn, understand, practice, try on, gain, inquire)

1. _____

2. _____

3. _____

Go share these with this individual now.

Keep in mind you can also ask this employee to do their own research to find answers. Just make sure to circle back to find out what they uncover.

G. Know When to Stop Investing in an Employee

If you have an employee who is struggling and you're wondering if it's time to move on, work through the questions below. The first set focuses on those who have a skills gap or performance issue. The second set focuses on those who have a challenging behavior or attitude.

Skills Gap or Performance Issue:

If you have an employee with a skills gap or a performance issue and you're not completely sure if the time has come to stop investing in their development, ask the following:

1. Is the missing skill a need to have or a nice to have? _____

2. Have you **clearly, directly and honestly** communicated how they do and do not meet expectations? _____

   ○ Did you provide specific examples? _____

   ○ Did you recommend how to change or ask them to research how to change? _____

   ○ Have you given them a real opportunity to improve? _____

   ○ If the gap is a "need to have", have you let them know the gap is job-threatening? _____

3. Once approached, has the employee sought ways to address this gap? _____

4. How long has this person not been a good fit? _____

5. Have you tried to change the position to accommodate this team member? _____

Remember: Find people who fit the position, not positions to fit the people.

6. Are there other areas in your organization where you could leverage their skills?
   _____

7. How much time, energy and resources have you put towards trying to help this individual? What are the concrete measurable outcomes of these efforts? What long-term changes or lack of changes have you witnessed?

   _____

   _____

8. On days when this person is giving you their best, is their performance at the level you need for this position? _____

   If you answered no, this person is not the right person for the position. Unfortunately a square peg can have the best intentions to fit into a round hole. They can try really hard. They might even find a way to wedge in a bit. But if they don't fit, they don't fit.

Toxic Character, Behavior or Attitude Issue:

If you have an employee with a character, behavior or attitude issue and you're not completely sure if the time has come to remove them from the team, ask the following:

1. How much time and energy have you spent contemplating this situation and/or talking about this individual to others to get clarity?

   _____

2. Because behavior can fluctuate, on their worst days how toxic are they? What is their behavior/way of being that's destructive?

   _____

   _____

3. How often do these days occur? _____ (Track them if you haven't.)

4. Now triple that cadence, because those are only the days and moments that you know about.
   _____

5. How long have you allowed this person to be on your team with this behavior? _____

6. Who does this behavior or attitude impact? How does it impact them?

   _____

   _____

7. What's the impact on overall team morale, productivity, collaboration, communication, sense of pride and shared identity?

   _____

   _____

8. Have you clearly, directly and honestly communicated to the individual the impact of their behavior or attitude? _____

   ○ Have you clearly, directly and honestly communicated that this behavior is unacceptable and won't be tolerated? _____

   ○ Did you provide specific examples? _____

   ○ Did you recommend how to change or ask them to research how to change? _____

   ○ Have you given them a real opportunity to improve? _____

   ○ Did you let them know it was job-threatening? _____

9. Once approached, has the employee sought ways to address this gap? _____

10. What would you tell a co-manager to do if this was their situation?

   _____

   _____

 Obstacle Obliterator: If this person is highly valuable to the organization because of their knowledge, connections, or sales production, you can be confident:

● If this person were gone tomorrow, you and your team would rally and figure it out. You're successful because you're resourceful.

● The negative impact this individual has on the rest of your employees' productivity, loyalty and morale is far more expensive than any financial gain they create.

● If this has been going on for a while, you don't even know the half of it. People stopped coming to you with their concerns long ago.

● They are not nearly as fabulous and valuable as you think they are.

H. Define Your Deal Breakers

Define what you're a stand against and what's intolerable and unacceptable in your organization. (Examples provided on pages 73 and 74 of *Culture Works*.) Consider including workplace bullying.

List eight items you won't tolerate:

1. _____

2. _____

3. _____

4. _____

5. _____

6. _____

7. _____

8. _____

Now, share these with your team. This not only sets clear expectations, it also creates a feeling of safety, belonging and pride.

 **Checklist:**

Check those action items you've completed.

A. _____ Shift from Shame to Support

B. _____ Apply the Workable Integrity Checklist

C. _____ Sip Truth Serum

D. _____ Clarify Character and Competency Expectations

E. _____ Teach Your Team the Peer Accountability Imperative

F. _____ Explain How to Change

G. _____ Know When to Stop Investing in an Employee

H. _____ Define Your Deal Breakers

Results or Shifts

What's one meaningful positive shift, outcome or result you've noticed due to these efforts?

_____

_____

_____

Now go share your success with someone and celebrate.

Your Top Three Takeaways:

1. _____

2. _____

3. _____

Deep Dive Discussion Guide

Bring your leadership and/or management team together and discuss:

What was your #1 takeaway or insight from Chapter 6?

_____

_____

_____

What did you take on or try on with your team? How did that go? What was harder than you expected? What was easier than you expected?

_____

_____

_____

What's one meaningful positive shift, outcome or result that came out of your efforts? (Pause to celebrate!) If applicable, what are you going to do to maintain, sustain and continue to nurture that outcome?

_____

_____

_____

What support or help would you like to request from this team? Advice? Best practices? Lessons learned? Being held accountable for following through on a commitment or making a habit stick?

_____

_____

_____

Chapter 7

Build Trust and Break Down Divisions

- How Much Do You Trust Your Team?
- Know Thyself
- Create This Trust-Building Habit
- Uncover Understanding
- Create Your Own Confessional Gong Venue
- Share Your Humanity
- Wipe the Slate Clean
- Bring Boomers and Millennials Together
- Go Speed Dating
- Enhance Workplace Camaraderie
- Checklist, Results and Takeaways
- Deep Dive Discussion Guide

Supervisor

Co-workers

Autonomy

Organizational Support

Organizational Fit

"The best way to find out if you can trust somebody is to trust them."

—Ernest Hemingway, novelist and journalist

A. How Much Do You Trust Your Team?

When you look at the Types of Trust listed below, in what areas do you trust your overall team on a scale of zero to three? In what areas don't you? Do you have reasons? Cite specific examples.

Absolute—3, Pretty confident—2, Not so much—1, Not at all—0

_____ **Work Ethic**—I trust you will carry your own weight and work hard.

_____ **Competency**—I trust you have the capacity and ability to do your job well.

_____ **Humility**—I trust you know your limits and will ask for help and guidance when you need it.

_____ **Ethics**—I trust you'll do the right thing.

_____ **Self Accountability**—I trust that if you make a mistake you'll own it and won't shift the blame.

_____ **Intentions**—I trust you are trying to do what's best for the organization as a whole.

_____ **Integrity**—I can count on you to do what you say you will do.

_____ **Honesty and Transparency**—I trust you're telling the truth and not lying by omission.

_____ **Thoughtfulness**—I trust you to consider the impact on others of your decisions and actions.

_____ **Alliance**—I trust you to have my back.

_____ **What Happens in Vegas**—I trust you will keep this in the utmost confidence.

_____ **Vulnerability**—I trust you won't judge me when I share personal challenges.

Hopefully most of your answers are twos and threes. If you have mostly ones, except for the last three on this list, your trust issues could have more to do with you than your team. What do you notice?

_____

_____

B. Know Thyself

As a general rule, when it comes to your team, would you say you trust easily? Or is it hard for you to trust? If you're not sure, ask your beloved or close friend what they think.

_____

If you trust easily, how is that expressed to your team through your leadership? Are you also good at holding people accountable?*

_____

_____

_____

*If you're easy to trust, but slow to hold people accountable when they're struggling, consider you may battle with the core desire to be "liked" by your team.

If it is hard for you to trust, would you say you struggle with:

- Micromanagement
- Letting go of control

- Perfectionism
- Delegation

If you answered yes to any of these, why?

_____

_____

If the reason you gave is from an earlier case in which someone deceived, misled or cheated you, consider not bringing your past into your future. Consider not applying that person's "wrongdoing" to all future innocents.

 Mini-Mantra: Live and lead for what's probable.

If your distrust isn't specific to a person, is it rooted in any of the following fears (also known as common human insecurities)?:

- Making a mistake.
- Being wrong.
- Not being good enough.
- Feeling excluded.
- Not looking good.
- Looking foolish or stupid.
- Feeling clueless or out of the loop.

Mindset Shift: Be self-aware. Notice when you feel hesitant to trust your team or to delegate. Pause and notice where that feeling is coming from. Is the hesitancy legitimate or simply an insecurity? Then choose based on who you believe yourself to be and how you want to lead, with an eye on empowering your team.

If you don't tend to notice your own hesitancy, notice when you're feeling overwhelmed or alone with all the responsibility. Ask yourself, how did I get here and who could help me if I let them?

 Remember: Your team will feel honored if you believe in them enough to let go and hand over the reins. Include them in both the authority and the responsibility. This is how employees gain a sense of ownership. More work responsibility, along with the authority that goes with it, creates a deeper sense of connection, obligation and pride.

 Mini-Mantra: We trust people who trust us.

Trust Biases: Are you aware of any of your own trust biases—where you tend to trust some people more easily than others, usually because they are similar to you? (For example—gender, age, education, weight, geography, religion, smoking preference, etc.)

_____

_____

First, make a short list of the team members you trust the most as well as a short list of those you trust the least.

Trust the Most	Trust the Least
_____	_____
_____	_____
_____	_____
_____	_____
_____	_____

What patterns, if any, do you notice? Do you have fact-based evidence to back your level of trust? Or would you say it's more of a gut feel? If it's a gut feel, investigate. Where does that feeling originate?

_____

_____

Remember: Trust a new employee until they prove themselves untrustworthy. Trust they have a good work ethic. Trust they want to do their best. By giving your trust, you are saying you believe in them and in their potential. For employees well past orientation, trust their ability in *how* to get the work done. Remember, our research indicated that one of the eight critical factors that makes employees feel good about coming to work is autonomy. Clarify expectations, define critical boundaries, encourage questions when they get stuck and then let them run with the task. Trust their ability to lead their work. Autonomy results from trust and spurs pride, ownership, self-confidence and creative problem solving.

Six Pro-Active Obstacle Obliterators: When you're struggling to trust someone:

1. Start from a place of curiosity rather than judgment. Seek to understand.

2. Don't question someone's intentions or assume mal-intent. When you question someone's intent, you question the core of their character. This will cause the relationship to go sideways faster than I can eat a chocolate cupcake.

3. Don't make an example out of one person.

4. Don't send a blanket email scolding or correcting the whole team for one person's way of being.

5. Don't say, "I don't trust you." Instead, be specific about both what you think the challenge at hand is and what you need from them.

6. Instead of asking "Who did it?" start with "Help me understand..." Seek solutions. "How did we get here?" "What do we need to do to avoid this in the future?"

Last, self reflect. Considering all of the above, is there anything you would like to shift regarding how you trust your team?

_____

_____

_____

C. Create This Trust-Building Habit

When your team comes to you with a problem, rather than giving them the answer, first ask, **"Well, what do you think?"** Listen, and as often as possible, empower their confidence and pluck by responding, "Sounds like a good option, go try it out and let me know how it goes." If it doesn't go perfectly or the way you would have done it, don't roast them! Praise what worked and guide what didn't. This not only demonstrates trust, it empowers your people to be better problem solvers. This also helps avoid the dreaded decision-making bottleneck.

 Bite-Size Step: Post, "Well what do you think?" in three places where you will see it daily. Read it aloud each morning for 19 days.

D. Uncover Understanding

Do you clash with a co-worker because you bring differing perspectives? Or do you have two team members whose opposing positions lead to stagnation, disarray or bad feelings rather than a thoughtful, cooperative outcome?

 If so, invite the other person to a conversation with the intention to better understand each other's perspective, approach, or ideology. No agenda. No convincing. Just sharing and seeking to understand why the other person believes what they believe.

 Invite this person now and get a time on your calendar.

E. Create Your Own Confessional Gong Venue

Remember the Confessional Gong? (Page 82 of *Culture Works* book)

Get a time on your calendar and invite two other leaders or managers to brainstorm how you could create a safe venue for your team to share mistakes and learn from one another.

_____

_____

_____

_____

F. Share Your Humanity

Do you have an open door policy, but only your trusted advisors give you the real scoop? Do you ask for feedback directly from your team, and receive little or nothing of consequence?

If you answered no to both of these, you can skip to the next exercise.

If you answered yes to either of these, do you:

- Give off an air of being too busy or seem impatient? _____
- Have your office door closed often? _____
- Struggle to keep confidences or talk about employees with other employees? _____
- Take things personally? _____
- Demonstrate intimidating or condescending body language? _____

If you answered yes to any of the above, start there.

If you answered no to all of the above, then chances are you're boxed in a boss stereotype. To get out of the box, share your humanity, demonstrate humility and be vulnerable.

On occasion, when the situation is appropriate, share how you're a real deal human being, warts and all. Share how you bleed. Reveal your insecurities. Admit to mistakes. Remind them that you don't have all the answers. Confess that sometimes you even question your judgment.

 Share: Pick a mistake you've made in the last six months that's impacted your team. In your next team meeting, take a few minutes at the end to name it, own it and apologize for it.

Mistake:

_____

 Add it to the agenda now—"5 minutes to touch base"

G. Wipe the Slate Clean

If your culture is toxic or if distrust is rampant, wipe the slate clean. It won't just go away with time. In fact, it festers.

This is equally true if your organization has baggage or mistakes from the past that are dredged up regularly.

Someone has to own the impact of the culture and that someone is you.

As the head honcho, you must apologize to the entire team—ideally at the same time. Describe in detail how the organization got here. Make eye contact, and pause to emphasize that you understand how serious and painful the situation has been for the team. Describe what it looks like and feels like and be candid in your description.

 With your whole team together:

1. **Describe the gory details.** Really. Everyone already knows them. They want to know YOU know them.
2. **Do not explain why or reason away why.** It makes you appear defensive and sounds like an "I'm sorry, but..."
3. **Acknowledge the impact.** Take this up a notch. The impact is deeper than you think or it's gained depth as the pain of time has seared it into the organization. Speak to how hard it has been for everyone.
4. **Apologize.** If you were part of leadership when things went sideways, own it. If you weren't, apologize on behalf of those who were. It is much easier to forgive and forget after a genuine apology.
5. **Recognize and thank those who endured.**
6. **Speak to the desired future in your next all-team meeting.** Do not address it during this gathering or it will feel like everything that came before wasn't genuine.
7. **Meaningfully paint the picture of the future** and what's possible in this second meeting.
8. **Get physically-demonstrated agreement.** Ask: "Please stand up (or raise your hand) if you're on board." Pause and survey the room, making kind eye contact with each individual. What if they don't respond? There are no guarantees, but every time I have made this recommendation, the entire team stands. The peer pressure and peer support for a better future override the stubborn.

H. Bring Boomers and Millennials Together

Do you have inter-generational drama? Especially between Boomers and Millennials? Ageism is common. This cuts both ways. Consider the stereotypical off-hand comments, "Millennials are entitled" or "Old people are clueless."

 Get a time on your calendar to bring the team together.

 Speak to the importance of age diversity, and to how ingenuity is fostered through the lens of differing perspectives. Talk through the following ways to demonstrate humility and respect, regardless of age:

- Acknowledge if you have less experience or comfort on a topic. Freely admit when you don't know something.

- Validate one another's contribution. Openly admire skills and knowledge.

- Include one another in conversations and seek advice and feedback.

- Seek to understand the others' perspective and be empathetic.

- Be curious about one another and find common ground—share stories, past experiences, aspirations.

- Never be dismissive or condescending.

- Assume it's NOT because of your age.

- Reach out to someone from another generation with the intention to learn both about, and from, one another.

These could apply to bringing together other factions, however they are particularly helpful with breaking down ageism.

Then run Speed Dating.

I. Go Speed Dating

I'm often asked for team-building exercises. While many are lackluster or forced fun, this one has never failed:

1. Print the questions on the next page—one set for each participant.

2. Have everyone stand and pair up, ideally with someone they don't know well. If there are an odd number of people, it's okay to have a threesome.

3. Give instructions:

   o Each couple will have a total of three minutes together.

   o You can start with any question you want.

   o You can cover all five questions or just one.

   o When I yell STOP, high five your partner.

   o Then switch and find a new partner.

   o We'll do three rounds.

   o GO! Then use your timer.

The room will get progressively loud, full of smiles and laughter.

If you want to run more than three rounds, run the first set of questions for the first three rounds, and the second set of questions for the last three rounds. Hand out the second set of questions right before the fourth round. Of course feel free to create your own questions!

First Set:

1. What would your friends or family say you're known for?

2. What's the most common misperception people have of you?

3. Find three things you two have in common.

4. In 60 seconds tell your life story in as much detail as possible.

5. Share an embarrassing or inspiring moment in your life.

Second Set:

1. What's something you've done that has expanded your comfort zone?

2. What's your favorite childhood memory?

3. What do you consider "paradise"?

4. What was your biggest challenge last year?

5. What's your favorite gift you've ever received/given?

J. Enhance Workplace Camaraderie

 Here's how both your on-site and remote teams can rock some serious camaraderie. Circle the three initiatives below that most appeal. Then pick one.

Which one did you choose?:

_____

 Schedule implementation time in your calendar now. Go get 'em tiger!

*   **Monday Morning Momentum.** For a few minutes have each team member share their weekend highlight as well as what they're looking to accomplish that week. This is a good time to leverage the "Cadence of Accountability" check-in as well.

*   **Fun and Fast:** Take a deep dive on a team member's personal interest in five minutes. Have one team member follow the Ignite format of sharing their knowledge on a topic of interest using 20 slides that auto-advance every 15 seconds. Examples at ignitetalks.io.

*   **Connect Four:** Set the expectation that each team member is responsible for getting to know better four of their cohorts each month. Schedule 30-minute "getting to know all about you" exchanges. Pairs can lean on the Speed Dating questions if they need fodder.

*   **Rose, Bud, Thorn:** Once a week, give everyone on the team three minutes at the beginning of the meeting to share their personal and professional Rose, Bud, Thorn as described on page 70 of this workbook.

*   **Check Everyone's Temperature:** Details on page 69.

*   **Show and Tell:** Have everyone give a video tour of their workspace. Or share their favorite meme or three items they'd save in a fire.

*   **Celebrate Wins:** Play "We are the Champions" by Queen and belt out together "No time for losers, 'cause we are the champions of the wooooorld." Be goofy and high five one another.

- **Leverage Music:** Do a conga line or the cupid shuffle, or the chicken dance together via video if you're remote. Or play the song "Jump"—Kriss Kross or Van Halen both work—and jump together.

- **Swap and Share:** Recipes. Coolest new app. Bucket lists. Your worst nightmare. Stress relief or time management tip. Favorite song.

- **Article Club:** Take turns sharing an *interesting* article that expands learning related to your work and have everyone read and discuss.

- **All Plaid Friday:** Or polka dot. Or ugly sweater. Or 70's. You get the idea.

- **JibJab:** Make a JibJab card for your team—super cheesy and it'll make them laugh.

- **Story Jam:** Pick a topic for the month and have everyone share a short story from their life. You can check out themoth.org for inspirational topics.

- **Bad Clean Jokes:** What did the cop say to her stomach? You're underavest.

- **Friday Afternoon Club:** If possible, have everyone end the week by gathering for a few minutes to share the highlight of their week and what they're up to for the weekend.

 Remember: If you have a remote team, make sure to implement the ideas on pages 91 and 92 of the *Culture Works* book to create a virtual team conducive to camaraderie.

 Checklist:

Check those action items you've completed or put N/A if not applicable.

A. _____ How Much Do You Trust Your Team?

B. _____ Know Thyself

C. _____ Create This Trust Building Habit

D. _____ Uncover Understanding

E. _____ Create Your Own Confessional Gong Venue

F. _____ Share Your Humanity

G. _____ Wipe the Slate Clean

H. _____ Team Generational Conversation

I. _____ Go Speed Dating

J. _____ Enhance Workplace Camaraderie

 Results or Shifts

What's one meaningful positive shift, outcome or result you've noticed due to these efforts?

_____

_____

_____

Now go share your success with someone and celebrate.

Your Top Three Takeaways:

1. _____

2. _____

3. _____

Deep Dive Discussion Guide

Bring your leadership and/or management team together and discuss:

What was your #1 takeaway or insight from Chapter 7?

_____

_____

_____

What did you take on or try on with your team? How did that go? What was harder than you expected? What was easier than you expected?

_____

_____

_____

What's one meaningful positive shift, outcome or result that came out of your efforts? Pause to celebrate! If applicable, what are you going to do to maintain, sustain and continue to nurture that outcome?

_____

_____

_____

What support or help would you like to request from this team? Advice? Best practices? Lessons learned? Being held accountable for following through on a commitment or making a habit stick?

_____

_____

_____

Chapter 8

Nurture Kind, Candid and Constructive Communication

- Dig Deeper

- Create Security and Belonging

- Listen to the Breadcrumbs

- Spur Behavior Shifts Through Public Praise

- Rein in Gossip

- Track Your Team's Temperature

- Open with Rose, Bud, Thorn

- Address Those Prone to Comparison

- Move Towards Taking It Personally

- Checklist, Results and Takeaways

- Deep Dive Discussion Guide

Supervisor

Co-workers

Organizational Support

Organizational Fit

Work-Family Climate

"How we believe others see us shapes who we are. We ride a wave of pride or get swallowed in a sea of embarrassment based on brief interactions that signal respect or disrespect....Civility lifts people. Incivility holds people down."

—Christine Porath, professor of management
at Georgetown University

A. Dig Deeper

The next time someone says, "We need better communication," don't roll your eyes. Instead dig deeper and don't accept generalities. Listen for nuance and keep digging until you get to the heart of this common surface comment. Ask:

- "Tell me more." Or "Oh?" These two simple phrases are powerful when followed only by your listening. These phrases and your silence give the other person the space to spill their real concerns.

- Can you give me some specific examples?

- What's really frustrating you?

B. Create Security and Belonging

Teams trust when they feel safe and in the loop. To create this sense of security and inclusion:

- Stay in consistent, clear communication with your team. Outline progress on quarterly goals. Speak to current financial health, successes, challenges, and what's being done about those challenges. Also speak to upcoming changes. Consider providing monthly updates on the "State of the Union." Solicit questions from the team beforehand and speak to those directly.

- Be transparent and forthcoming when the organization faces a dilemma (sales dive, a competitor gains coveted ground, or a client threatens to sue.)

- Once briefed on the challenge, include your team in problem solving. You can then rally your team's support and leverage their insight.

- Share when you can't share due to regulatory, strategic or contract reasons.

 Obstacle Obliterator: Communication does not consist of cc'ing everyone on every e-mail nor of describing the details of every dilemma. Think of it as letting your team know the weather report. Share what's anticipated so they know if they need galoshes and aren't left in the cold rain while you're sporting your anorak. Also keep in mind, the bigger the challenge or the change, the more you have to be repetitive in your communication. A flood requires more heads up than a spring rain shower.

Mini-Mantra: Regularly share the weather report.

How do you consistently communicate with your team so they feel "in the loop?" Has anyone on your team recently felt blindsided? If so, what could you have said beforehand to mitigate that surprise? Can you think of a simple, meaningful way in which you could step up, or deepen, your communication with your team?

_____

_____

_____

 Remember: Surprises at work are unnerving. Eyebrows raise when there's an **unexpected** _addition or reduction_ in staff, compensation, workload, product offerings, project scope or timing. The impact ranges from feeling miffed and annoyed to feeling blindsided and betrayed. Productivity plunges as employees try to regain their footing.

Remember: In a culture of uncertainty, closing a door signals the sky is falling. Closed doors seed and grow unseen mistrust. The unknown is scary.

C. Listen to the Breadcrumbs

The next time a team member lightly knocks on your door *with a slightly pained expression* and asks if you have a minute *and* says they don't want to bother you or it's not that big of a deal:

- Wholeheartedly pause what you're doing (tough to do, I know)
- Gladly wave them in
- Be fully present
- Actively listen

Significant morale intel is likely at hand.

 Mini-Mantra: Listen to the breadcrumbs.

 Bite-Size Step: If you struggle to pause, post where you're most often interrupted, "STOP and listen to the breadcrumbs."

 Obstacle Obliterator: Overall, don't encourage interruptions. Implement the "office hours" recommendation on page 140 of *Culture Works*. When "office hours" are in place, the knock on your door becomes even more pertinent.

Have you had any breadcrumbs as of late? Did you listen or brush them off? Do you need to go back and see if it leads to a loaf of bread?

_____

_____

_____

D. Spur Behavior Shifts Through Public Praise

Overall I tend to caution against public praise from a supervisor to a team member *unless you're looking to shift a habit or commonly accepted routine of the team.* Praising a desired behavior, attitude or performance publically tells the rest of the team to get on board. For example, if your team struggles with being candid about concerns, the next time someone is courageous and candid—perhaps sharing feedback, a challenge or a mistake—thank them for their frankness in front of the team. This sends a clear message to your team that it's not only safe to share these items, but that it's also something you genuinely value.

What would you like to see more of in your team? Sense of urgency? Solution- oriented? Perseverance? Prompt and prepared? Who on your team does this well? Pick a specific instance and praise that in your next team meeting. Continue to look for opportunities to praise this behavior until it becomes a regular part of your team's way of being.

_____

_____

_____

Obstacle Obliterator: If no one on your team initially exemplifies the behavior you would like to see, take a deeper dive. Meet with your team and:

● Share the desired behavior or attitude you would like to see.

● Share why it's important. Ideally hook into the mission.

● Provide specific concrete examples of what this behavior or attitude looks like in practice.

● Share a story of how someone else has exhibited this behavior (a colleague, a competitor, a celebrity) and the benefits that resulted.

E. Rein in Gossip

Does your team struggle with gossip and drama? _____

If not, skip this exercise.

If they do, evaluate yourself on the following on a scale of zero to three:

3—I rock this one!
2—I feel pretty good on this one.
1—Yeah, this one needs some attention.
0—Yikes, I really struggle here.

1. _____ **I'm transparent with my team.**
   I communicate "the weather," including opportunities, challenges and changes. I share the strategic plan as well as the financials with my team. My team feels like they know the whole truth and feels a strong sense of security and inclusion. I do not have secrets, unwritten rules, or un-communicated motives.

2. _____ **I'm consistent in my commitments and my actions.**
   My team knows I will do what I say I'm going to do and if I'm unable to follow through, I communicate this as well. I do not hesitate to apologize for my mistakes.

3. _____ **I seek my team's input and feedback before and during any significant change.**
   Whenever possible, I include employees in decision-making. I take employee suggestions and concerns seriously and make sure to complete the response loop by communicating actions taken as a result of their input.

4. _____ **I provide real opportunities for people to connect, share, and learn about one another.**
   Whether through a May Madness foosball tournament, speed dating exercise or a simple lunch and learn, I make sure to provide time and venues for camaraderie building.

Remember: Because gossip is one of the quickest and easiest ways to emotional intimacy, these real opportunities for people to connect are critical to avoiding gossip's sticky social super glue trap.

5. _____ **I promptly address employees who are not performing.**
   I guide, coach and support my team in being the best they can be. When an individual on the team is struggling to fit, whether it's a competency issue or a character issue, I address it as soon as possible. This includes swiftly addressing gossip, triangulation and drama.

6. _____ **I listen to the breadcrumbs.**
   When an employee comes to me with a concern I pause, actively listen, take it seriously and then follow-up.

Now give a similar evaluation below to your team.

3—Most definitely.

2—Most days.

1—Some days.

0—Mmm...not so much.

1. _____ My supervisor is transparent about opportunities, challenges and changes. I feel like I know what's going on.

2. _____ My supervisor's commitments and actions align.

3. _____ My supervisor seeks the team's input and feedback before and during any significant change.

4. _____ My supervisor provides real opportunities for our team to connect, share, and learn about one another.

5. _____ My supervisor promptly addresses employees who are not performing or who are bringing morale down.

6. _____ When I have a concern, I feel like my supervisor really listens to me and takes my feedback seriously.

Simply because of the power differential, know that a two from a team member often means a one.

On any of the statements for evaluation, did you have ones on your evaluation or twos on theirs? If so, which statements?

_____

_____

Awareness is the first step.

What are three specific bite-size steps you will take to rein in gossip?

1. _____

2. _____

3. _____

Do any of these steps require you to block out time? If so, block it now.

E. Track Your Team's Temperature

Remember: Emotions are information. They should not be suppressed or disregarded. You want to know if someone on your team is elated. You want to know if someone is frustrated or disappointed. Emotions are also contagious. Which works great if joy is in the air, not so great if apathy is spreading.

Every few weeks, take your team's temperature by asking the questions below and track it.

1. **On a scale of 1–10 how are you doing this week?**
   Note, usually 7 is indicative of "fine." Not lovin' it, not hatin' it. Less than 7 is usually concerning, while more than 7 suggests the individual is truly in a "good space." Keep in mind, for your analytical types, 5 is "fine."

2. **What contributes to that number?**
   This question allows for discovery without judgment. Here is where you learn if their response is based on personal or professional conditions or a combo.

3. If it's six or higher, ask, **what would make it a plus one?**

4. If it's five or lower, ask, **is there anything I can do to support you?**

5. When the number is higher or lower than last time, ask, **"What shifted?"**

Initials	Date _____	Date _____	Date _____
1.* _____	_____	_____	_____
2. _____	_____	_____	_____
3. _____	_____	_____	_____
4. _____	_____	_____	_____
5. _____	_____	_____	_____
6. _____	_____	_____	_____
7. _____	_____	_____	_____
8. _____	_____	_____	_____
9. _____	_____	_____	_____

*On the first line, track your number.

What patterns do you notice, if any?

_____

_____

G. Open with Rose, Bud, Thorn

Open a meeting with a round robin of Rose, Bud, Thorn. Have each team member take one minute to share:

- Rose: Best thing that's happened in the last week.
- Bud: What you're most looking forward to in the coming week.
- Thorn: Biggest challenge in the coming week.

 In which meeting will you try this on? _____

H. Address Those Prone to Comparison

If you have a team member who is prone to comparison or scorekeeping:

1. Support them in taking personal responsibility for what they can control. Depending on the area being compared, recommend they ask for what they need, increase their ROI to the organization, or choose differently.

2. Express your expectation for them to wish the best for their co-workers and not to begrudge their peers for progress, success, or good fortune.

3. Focus on being just, not fair. Fairness is an impossible trap.

4. Explain the "why" behind decisions. Especially around such topics as new hires, promotions, compensation changes, new resource purchases, and work schedule changes.

 Remember: Comparisons and scorekeeping are often rooted in a lack of understanding. Why did they get it and I didn't? Proactively answer this question before it's asked. If an employee sees how and why a decision is made, they may still wish things were different, but they no longer make others wrong for having what they want. When they understand how and why someone received a promotion, a new computer, or a flexible work schedule, they understand the equation and are empowered to make it happen for themselves.

Do you have someone who is prone to comparison or scorekeeping? _____

 If so, determine now how you can keep these four steps close at hand when the timing is right.

I. Move Towards Taking It Personally

Bring your team together for ten minutes and share the value of "taking it personally" and discuss:

What would it look like if we actually took feedback personally? Not by being offended per se, but by really taking it to heart and considering its validity.

Think about it.

When someone gives you "constructive" feedback, it's personal.

When someone suddenly takes you off a pet project, it's personal.

When someone questions your motives, it's personal.

We're told not to take things personally, especially in the workplace. I suggest instead you **take it to heart,** especially if it's tough to hear. **Feel the sting.** Don't react. Don't run. Don't hide. Don't justify and defend. Just see if it resonates uncomfortably.

If it does, **thank the person** for their candor and change your attitude or behavior. To gain clarity on how to move forward, you may want to ask this individual, or those who stand for your success, "What would a shift look like?"

If it doesn't resonate, lead with curious inquiry rather than an accommodating apology. Ask for more clarity, "Help me understand, why this is your experience of me? What am I missing?" You can always let them know you don't see what they see, that while it doesn't resonate you're willing to try it on over the next few weeks and will circle back.

Many would tell you just to "let it go." The truth is, we don't. We fester. We close off. We fake. We may even obsess. Until you've actually considered the potential validity of what's been posed, you can't let it go. So consider it. Respond thoughtfully.

And remember...

When someone praises you, it's personal.

When someone promotes you, it's personal.

When you're asked to head up a project, it's personal.

Then discuss.

When will you try this mindset shift on with your team? _____

Checklist:

Check those action items you've completed or put N/A if not applicable.

A. _____ Dig Deeper

B. _____ Create Security and Belonging

C. _____ Listen to the Breadcrumbs

D. _____ Spur Behavior Shifts Through Public Praise

E. _____ Rein in Gossip

F. _____ Track Your Team's Temperature

G. _____ Open with Rose, Bud, Thorn

H. _____ Address Those Prone to Comparison

I. _____ Move Towards Taking It Personally

Results or Shifts

What's one meaningful positive shift, outcome or result you've noticed due to these efforts?

_____

_____

_____

Now go share your success with someone and celebrate.

Your Top Three Takeaways:

1. _____

2. _____

3. _____

Deep Dive Discussion Guide

Bring your leadership and/or management team together and discuss:

What was your #1 takeaway or insight from Chapter 8?

_____

_____

_____

What did you take on or try on with your team? How did that go? What was harder than you expected? What was easier than you expected?

_____

_____

_____

What's one meaningful positive shift, outcome or result that came out of your efforts? Pause to celebrate! If applicable, what are you going to do to maintain, sustain and continue to nurture that outcome?

_____

_____

_____

What support or help would you like to request from this team? Advice? Best practices? Lessons learned? Being held accountable for following through on a commitment or making a habit stick?

_____

_____

_____

Chapter 9

Repair Relationships

- Know One Another's Conflict Styles

- Envision Your Team's Relationship Matrix

- Uncover the Source of the Relationship Breakdown

- Pick a Rock, Any Rock

- Take Four Steps Out of Funkytown

- Train Your Entire Team on the Funkytown Process

- Resolve Conflict Between Two Employees

- Checklist, Results and Takeaways

- Deep Dive Discussion Guide

Supervisor   **Co-workers**   **Organizational Support**   **Organizational Fit**

"You must love truth more than you love saving face."

—Fred Kofman, philosopher and Vice President at Linkedin

Mini-Mantra: Bear hug conflict.

A. Know One Another's Conflict Styles

 Schedule 30 minutes with your team. Date and time: _____

 Share with your team your desire for everyone to know their own go-to conflict style as well as one another's default. Explain the advantages of knowing one another's conflict style:

1. When we know our own conflict style, we can be self-aware. This allows us to choose a different reaction and response. When our lizard brain wants to override rationale, self-awareness creates receptivity to a peer waving the white flag. Letting us know we've gone into flight or fight mode.

2. Knowing one another's style gives us an edge as a team. We know when a co-worker has been seduced by their conflict style. Nothing constructive can be accomplished when someone is in this state. Awareness allows us to stop discussions that have entered the no-fly zone before they cause irreparable harm.

3. When someone is stuck, you have to stop the conversation. Look them in the eye. Gently say, *"No one is attacking you.* I really want to work with you to figure out a solution." Let them take a deep breath and see if they can come back and be present. If so, regroup, starting with your intention. If not, reschedule.

4. Let your team know one conflict style isn't better than the other.

5. Share with your team the most common conflict styles of:

   o **Get defensive** (fight). This looks like stepping forward, getting louder, using defensive statements, blaming others, indignation, getting blustery with large hand and arm gestures.

   o **Shut down** (flight). This is stepping back, crossing your arms, trying to melt into the wallpaper, "lights are on but no one's home" look in your eyes, looking down, avoiding eye contact, waiting for it to be over, tuning out, closed body language, walking away, silence.

   o **Passive aggressive** (combo). In this mode, you have a snarky conversation in your head about what you would say in response, rolling your eyes, steely staring, huffing "whatever," short interjections of sarcasm, saying one thing and meaning another, under the breath comments, closed body language.

6. Ask your team, "When it comes to work and conflict, which of these do you think is your go-to conflict style when you're not being your best self?" Clarify you're speaking about those times when your nervous system takes the wheel and your mental capacity drains. Adrenaline is pumping through your veins and all reasoning takes a back seat. When we *are* our best selves we're grounded, committed to a resolution and receptive.

7. Ask, is it different with your peers vs. someone in authority? Capture their answers below and share the list with the entire team. Make sure to let people know that if they find reality is different from their perception, they can always update the list.

Name	Peer Go-To Conflict Style	Authority Go-To Conflict Style
1. _____	_____	_____
2. _____	_____	_____
3. _____	_____	_____
4. _____	_____	_____
5. _____	_____	_____
6. _____	_____	_____
7. _____	_____	_____
8. _____	_____	_____
9. _____	_____	_____

*On the last line, list your style.

B. Envision Your Team's Relationship Matrix

For those of you who are more visual or artistically inclined, consider drawing this dynamic. Heads up though, it can get a bit messy.

For the rest of you, imagine:

1. Your team sitting in a circle.

2. The relationships between each person to every other person.

3. For those relationships that are strong, there's a thick wire.

4. For those that are strained, weak or recovering, the wire is thin and perhaps brittle or taut with tension.

5. For those relationships that are new, there's a dotted line for the wire hasn't quite taken shape yet.

6. What rocks are in the space? What unresolved negative experiences, judgments or filters exist between people on your team? Imagine the various sized pebbles, rocks and boulders weighing down the wires and complicating communication. List the four heaviest rocks here:

   1. _____

   2. _____

   3. _____

   4. _____

7. Are any of the relationships broken or at the breaking point? If so, which ones?

   _____

   _____

8. Is there anything else you noticed in doing this exercise?

   _____

   _____

C. Uncover the Source of the Relationship Breakdown

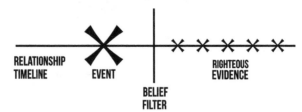

Remember: Most relationship breaks occur in a single moment or event resulting in a negative belief about the other person. We then see that person through that belief, through that filter, and continue to look for evidence to support that belief. Take your four heaviest rocks listed on the previous page and write down if there is an event that led to their existence:

Rock #1: _____

Rock #2: _____

Rock #3: _____

Rock #4: _____

Put a star next to those you *know* this is how the rock was created and an x next to those you *think* you know how the rock was created. Circle any of the rocks that are between you and another person.

D. Pick a Rock, Any Rock

If none of the rocks above are between you and another team member, is there a rock between you and another co-worker in your organization? If not, is there one between you and someone outside of work? The reason I ask—understanding the Funkytown process and supporting your team in learning the Funkytown process is most effective when...you got it, you actually go through the process. Yay! You knew this challenge was good for something.

Write the initials of the person you're sideways with here: _____

Just a reminder, Funkytown is the place where the rock lives. It's where there's unspoken or unresolved tension, hurt feelings, anger or confusion. The relationship is sideways.

Looking at the list below, circle or add to the bottom the most common reason you use to avoid talking to this person about the wonkiness in the space:

- It's just not worth it.
- It's not my place or job to tell them.
- It's just easier to do myself.
- I don't like conflict.
- I don't know how they will react.
- I *know* how they will react.
- I don't want to cause problems.
- They're just a jerk.
- Nothing would change anyway.
- It'll just make the situation worse.

● I don't want to hurt their feelings.

● _____

This is the reason you give for actively choosing to stay in Funkytown.

If it applies, and you know it, name the event in which the relationship broke and the filter you see that person through as a result of that experience:

_____

_____

How would you describe your experience of why the relationship is sideways:

_____

_____

_____

_____

*If you're feeling really triggered, you may need to write it ALL out. Get ALL that toxic heavy messiness out on paper. In which case, go grab a scratch paper (rather than a computer) and dump and rant until it's out of you and safely on paper. Be as raw as you can—this is for your eyes only. This can be ridiculously cathartic and dissipate the toxic internal intensity of the outrage, indignation or resentment.

E. Take Four Steps Out of Funkytown

The rewards of getting out of Funkytown are enormous. Ease of work and communication is one. Liberating the daily dread of "dealing" with the other person and feeling good about coming to work is another. However the most meaningful benefit is the freedom to be the person you believe yourself to be.

So how do you get from here to there? Take these four key steps.

Make sure you have time to thoughtfully complete steps 1–3 of this exercise. Set aside at least an hour. If you don't have an hour now, pause and find (or make) an hour in the next couple of days. Hold this time sacred. This is a priority.

1. **Self Reflection**

    a. **Evaluate why this individual hits a nerve.** Take some time to cull through your annoyed mind— your thoughts, behaviors, past experiences, insecurities and fears.

        o   What is triggering you?

        o   Where are you hooked?

        o   Does this experience bring to light something you would prefer hidden?

        o   Are you embarrassed about how you handled the situation?

        o   Are you the common denominator in similar experiences with others in your life?

        _____

        _____

        _____

        _____

b. **Let go of the anger.** If you come from a place of anger, your co-worker will run to the safety of their conflict style. This could look like mirroring your aggression or getting quiet and nodding in response, neither of which is productive. It makes the conversation all about you, your anger and how you're a jerk, reducing your co-worker's ability to take responsibility for their role.

Anger is an easier form of expression than fear or hurt. Fear and hurt require vulnerability. Vulnerability is foundational for a real deal conversation. To uncover vulnerability, **ask, "How do I feel?" Then ask a few more times.** The deeper you go, the easier it is for the other person to relate. Perhaps you feel embarrassed, ignored, shocked, ashamed, stupid, confused, disappointed or disrespected. These are all feelings we've painfully held at one point or another. Instead of feeling attacked, your co-worker can feel empathy.

How do you feel? **Keep peeling back the layers.**

_____

_____

c. **Let go of assumptions.** We get in trouble when we let our imagination fill in the blanks—also known as assumptions. Know there's a good chance you're missing a piece of information.

Ask:

o **What are the facts of the situation—***as you understand them?*

o What are you confused about?

o Also, did you make an assumption or fabricate meaning?

_____

_____

_____

_____

d. **Shortcuts after self-reflection:**

Clean it up. If you already know you're the source of the problem, own it. You're not the first person who defended and deflected when someone pointed out your error. Apologize for the impact you had on the other person—the sooner the better.

If you think it's all in your head, ask. If you think you're making an assumption, go to the other person and ask, "Is there any truth in this?"

With either of these you can skip the last three steps.

2. **Mentally Prepare How You Will Show Up**

a. **Be clear about your intentions and imagine your ideal outcome.** Ideally, you want to share your perspective, and understand the other person's perspective, about why things went sideways and then together figure out how to repair the relationship. An ideal outcome may be as simple as having a good working relationship with this person.

Your intention: _____

Your ideal outcome: _____

_____

b. **Let go of assumptions about what will happen.** How many times have you had an argument with this person BEFORE you've even started talking to them? You did a fantastic job playing both parts of the conversation. You now have it all figured out. You know exactly how it's going to go. We all do this. **Ultimately you don't know how this person will react.** If you're thinking, I've tried to talk to this person before and they're always defensive, chances are you tried once and didn't follow these steps. Be open to the possibility this will be a positive exchange. Your ideal outcome is, after all, possible.

What assumptions do you need to let go?

_____

_____

c. **Come from a place of genuine curiosity.** Start in humble wonderment rather than knowing judgment. The phrases "can you help me understand" or "I was curious why" are powerful especially when facts follow. Your tone is important. You can ask through gritted teeth and furrowed brow, or with an open face expressing a true desire to understand.

Will you come from a place of curiosity and a desire to understand? _____

d. **Trust the other person's intentions.** Most people in their heart of hearts don't intend harm. They try to do the best they can. When bad behavior does occur, often the core motivator is fear, shame or a desire to prove oneself. Be compassionate and assume positive intent.

What do you think are the other person's intentions?

_____

_____

e. **Identify common ground and be a stand.** Instead of focusing on differences, look for common ground. What do you both care about? Family? Kids? Your city? The mission of the organization? Trying to make a living? Be a stand for what you both care about that's more far-reaching than the spat between you two. "We both care about this place and want to see it succeed." "We both care about this team." "We both have families we're trying to support." "We're both trying to do the best we can do."

Common Ground: _____

_____

3. **Invite Them to the Conversation**

    Here's where the rubber meets the road. Until now, it's been all you, self-reflecting and mentally preparing. This is the shortest and hardest step. Whenever you invite someone to a conversation there is a possibility your invitation will be declined. Yet this is where the real deal magic begins. Without this step, all your preparation is wasted.

    You want your invitation to be simple, short and relaxed. Feel free to refer to the examples on page 119 of _Culture Works_.

Follow these five steps:

1. Say exactly and simply what's amiss.

2. Express humility.*

3. Express your intention.

4. Ask for their participation.

5. Define a good time to meet face to face.

*You must include humility for the invitation to work. Expressing humility creates a critical opening in the conversation for new awareness and thus a new outcome. Humility admits to the possibility that your assumptions may be inaccurate. Humility also consists of owning your role. This vulnerability allows the other person to reflect, acknowledge and be honest about their own assumptions and role. Examples:

- I haven't been exactly warm and fuzzy.

- Maybe I'm off base.

- I'm confused.

Write a draft of your invitation so it rolls off your tongue more casually.

_____

_____

_____

_____

Make sure your invitation does not include any of the following:

- Say, "We need to meet," "We need to talk."

- Try to be funny.

- Couch your communication.

- Get into the weeds of the situation.

Congratulations, the time to leave Funkytown is close at hand.

Obstacle Obliterator: What happens if someone doesn't accept your invitation? While rare, this could happen. Stay grounded. Stay committed. There is a good chance it's their conflict style speaking. Respond, "Know my invitation stands. I really would like to have a good working relationship with you. Whenever you're ready to talk, I'll be here." A few weeks later they'll likely ask you to go grab lunch.

Obstacle Obliterator: What if the person I'm in Funkytown with is my boss? Remember: like all of us, bosses are simply fallible human beings unaware of their own blind spots. Just like you would for a co-worker, be a stand for their success. It just requires a bit more courage on your part. Unfortunately few leaders get this type of direct feedback because of employees' fear of authority. Because leaders play such a critical role and have such a large impact, they need to hear from you. If you're kind, candid and constructive, if you show up with humility and curiosity, a leader will welcome your input, and your bravery. You may be surprised to end up as one of the CEO's trusted advisors.

4. **Have the Conversation**

   The majority of the conversation is giving voice to what you uncovered in steps one and two. Review your mental preparation before the meeting. Lead the meeting since you provided the invitation. Set the tone. Speak slowly and thoughtfully. Keep your intention to understand and to learn at the forefront. Look them in the eye and open the conversation:

   ○ **Acknowledge common ground.** Name what you both care about that's more important than your discord.

   ○ **Restate your intentions.** Repeat the one you stated in your invitation.

- Restate exactly and simply what's amiss.

- Define, *as you understand it,* the facts of what happened. And ask, "Is that accurate? Am I missing a piece?"

- Speak to the impact the discord has had on you.

- Own your part in the situation.

- Reveal assumptions. Then ask, "Are these assumptions correct? Or am I off base?"

- Express vulnerability. Phrases to consider on page 121 of *Culture Works.*

- Be curious and ask softball questions, "What's been the impact on you? What's been your understanding and your experience?"

- Listen for understanding. Listen like there is no one else in the world and nowhere else in the world you'd rather be.

- Stay steady. The other person may get defensive. Continue to wave the white flag and be a stand for the relationship.

- Consider solutions together and make requests. What do each of you need to do moving forward?

Helpful examples are on pages 121 and 122 of *Culture Works.*

 Obstacle Obliterator: You may be tempted to wait or hope it just goes away. Yet, remember, what you're up to in the world is bigger than this discord. Your time, mind space and energy are spent better elsewhere. By choosing to have this conversation, even if it goes awry, you can let go knowing you tried. You chose to be the person you believe yourself to be.

 Remember:

"Promise me you will not spend so much time treading water and trying to keep your head above the waves that you forget, truly forget, how much you have always loved to swim."

-**Tyler Knott Gregson,** poet and photographer

F. Train Your Entire Team on the Funkytown Process

If your team struggles with gossip, triangulation, grudges, "bad blood" or drama, lay down the groundwork from page 48 of this workbook—Teach Your Team the Peer Accountability Imperative. Then train your entire team on the Funkytown process for when a relationship goes sideways. This creates an empowering context of shared language, understanding and commitment to keep rocks out of the space.

Schedule 90 minutes to train your team, date and time: _____

BTW—you could also set aside 2.5 hours and cover peer accountability, conflict styles and the Funkytown training all together.

G. Resolve Conflict Between Two Employees

In Exercise B, you listed the four heaviest rocks, as well as those relationships between team members that are broken or at the breaking point.

If you have two team members where the impact and thus the urgency is too great for you to first train the team and then count on the two of them to work through it, mediate the conflict.

 You will need to schedule:

- Two 10 minute meetings—one with each of them—Friday
- Two 90 minute meetings—one with each of them—Tuesday
- One, two hour meeting with both of them—Thursday or Friday

1. Meet with each person individually. Do not mince words. Communicate:

   o This isn't working.

   o The impact their infighting has on you, their co-workers, your customers and the organization's reputation.

   o Empathy for what you imagine the impact must be on them.

   o How this conflict ultimately undermines the work and the mission.

   o This continued discord is no longer an option.

   o You value each one's contribution to the organization.

   o Each one of them must be committed to a resolution and be willing to have the tough conversations to get there.

   o Ask them both to go home, sleep on it and return in a couple of days with a commitment to working towards a successful working relationship, or you'll need to consider other alternatives.

2. If one of them gets belligerent and launches into how it's the other person's fault and how maybe they need to find another job, let them.

3. If both express interest in reconciliation, let them know you will be meeting with them together to resolve old grudges and address areas of misunderstanding and avoid triggers. Then meet with them individually and ask the questions below and take copious notes. Note heavy word choice or repeated phrases.

   o How do you feel about the other person?

   o How do you think the other person feels about you? Why do you think this and what do you know to be fact?

   o When was the first time you realized this person was someone you struggle to get along with?

   o What does the other person do or say that really bothers you? What triggers you?

   o What do you think you do or say that frustrates the other person?

   o Do you trust the other person wants what's best for the team and the organization?

   o Do you think the other person trusts you want what's best for the team and the organization?

   o What do you appreciate about the other person?

   o What is your role in this situation? How have you contributed?

   o Do you owe the other person an apology?

   o What could you do to improve this relationship?

Person One:

_____

_____

_____

_____

_____

_____

_____

_____

Person Two:

_____

_____

_____

_____

_____

_____

_____

_____

_____

4. Now look at the information you garnered from each individual.

   o What do you notice? What bridges do you see?

   o What are they each feeling?

   o What filters are they seeing one another through?

   o Where are the REAL contentious pitfalls in the relationship, the source, not just the symptoms? Was there an event that started this whole debacle?

   o What dynamics are at play?

   o What is the genuine hurt behind the stories?

Now, think about how you will bring these insights to the table. As the facilitator, your language is key. Choose language that accurately reflects what was said and allows for consideration and conversation.

_____

_____

_____

_____

_____

_____

_____

_____

5. In the meeting with the two of them:

- Let them know you are truly committed to the success of their relationship.

- Start with what they both appreciate about one another.

- Then ease into the key areas of concern and contention. Make sure to name vulnerable feelings, what they each named as far as how they contributed to the discord, and what they each are requesting from one another.

- Also if there is a single event in which the relationship broke, go back and unpack that event and find the misunderstanding.

- Make sure not to back down. Be brave and don't let them appease, acquiesce or placate.

- Resolve with apologies, agreements and tangible commitments. Write down the triggers, agreements and commitments in a touchstone document for the two them to reference in the future.

Triggers, Agreements and Commitments:

_____

_____

_____

_____

_____

_____

_____

_____

_____

_____

_____

_____

_____

_____

_____

Checklist:

Check those action items you've completed or put N/A if not applicable.

A. _____ Know One Another's Conflict Styles

B. _____ Envision Your Team's Relationship Matrix

C. _____ Uncover the Source of the Relationship Breakdown

D. _____ Pick a Rock, Any Rock

E. _____ Take Four Steps Out of Funkytown

F. _____ Train Your Entire Team on the Funkytown Process

G. _____ Resolve Conflict Between Two Employees

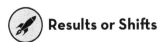

Results or Shifts

What's one meaningful positive shift, outcome or result you've noticed due to these efforts?

_____

_____

Now go share your success with someone and celebrate.

Your Top Three Takeaways:

1. _____

2. _____

3. _____

Deep Dive Discussion Guide

Bring your leadership and/or management team together and discuss:

What was your #1 takeaway or insight from Chapter 9?

_____

_____

_____

What did you take on or try on with your team? How did that go? What was harder than you expected? What was easier than you expected?

_____

_____

_____

What's one meaningful positive shift, outcome or result that came out of your efforts? Pause to celebrate! If applicable, what are you going to do to maintain, sustain and continue to nurture that outcome?

_____

_____

_____

What support or help would you like to request from this team? Advice? Best practices? Lessons learned? Being held accountable for following through on a commitment or making a habit stick?

_____

_____

_____

Chapter 10

Create Culture Conducive to Change

- Evaluate Your Team's Change Reaction
- Implement a Change Upgrade
- Answer to Actualize Successful Significant Change
- Checklist, Results and Takeaways
- Deep Dive Discussion Guide

| Supervisor | Meaning/
Job Fit | Impact | Organizational
Support | Organizational
Fit |

"Are you green and growing or ripe and rotting?"

—Ray Kroc, McDonald's mogul

A. Evaluate Your Team's Change Reaction

How well does your team react to change? Do they get on board easily? Are they nimble, excited to innovate, and willing to slog through the awkward learning curve? Or do they groan every time you suggest a new initiative? Or perhaps they placate you, nodding in agreement, with no intention of shifting and hoping to wait you out? Or are they simply burnt out on change?

List three specific instances when your team has and has not embraced change:

1. _____   1. _____

2. _____   2. _____

3. _____   3. _____

Do you notice any patterns?

_____

_____

If your team embraces change, thank them. A lot. Speak to specifics and let them know how much you appreciate their willingness to step up to the plate even when it's outside of their comfort zone.

 If your team struggles with change or is feeling depleted from change, schedule an hour with your team to implement a change upgrade. Date and time: _____

 Remember: We are creatures of our own competency. Nobody likes feeling stupid. For those who block change or drag their feet, have empathy, but not patience.

B. Implement a Change Upgrade

Ideally have a conversation with your team to shift their perspective on change when you're not looking to make a new change right away. Otherwise this exchange can be perceived as self-serving and manipulative.

If your team is feeling reasonably burnt out on change, then this is less about shifting their perspective and more about appreciating creating a safe place to kvetch, buoy their spirits and prepare them for the next round.

1. To set up the context and get your team engaged in the discussion, **have your team take Ariane de Bonovoisin's "The First 30 Days Change Quiz"** http://images.barnesandnoble.com/pimages/resources/pdf/Change_Quiz.pdf?cds2Pid=17007&linkid=1401682

    Then discuss as a team:

    o   In general, are you someone who likes change or can't stand it? Why?

    o   What changes have you enjoyed at our organization?

    o   What changes have been frustrating, hard or scary?

 Then Share:

2. **If we don't play, if we don't consistently innovate, we will lose.** Share the sad stories of Blockbuster and Kodak who didn't play in the world of online streaming media and digital photography. They lost. Think of Facebook who moved beyond the comfort of colleges. It won. Think of Google which expanded beyond the role of search engine with Adwords. They won. Yahoo wallflowered.

 Mini-Mantra: If we don't play we can't win.

3. **Tell your team you wish all change could be chosen, known and controllable.** Promise you will do your best to keep them apprised of upcoming changes. When possible you will seek and consider their input prior to taking action. However, also mention change is often unpredictable and in moments of chaos and crisis you need their help and support.

4. **Speak to why change is positive even when outcomes are unknown.** Change challenges us to expand our comfort zone. Butterflies keep us on our toes. We gain opportunities to learn and uncover valuable insights. Change is career development at its best.

5. **Address the reality of change.** It's not perfect. Sometimes it looks like two stumbles forward, one step to the side and one step back. The team may need to try things on and see if they fit. When they don't, it's a great example of failing forward. Tell stories about changes in the past that were successful and speak about ones that weren't and what you learned as a result. With particularly difficult changes, make sure you speak to the discomfort. Don't soft sell it.

 Mini-Mantra: Try, learn, adjust.

6. **Underscore the humor and humanity of change.** Emphasize that when you go through change, you're all going through it together. Change is a journey. Acknowledge that sometimes change is just messy. Ask your team to keep their sense of humor. Stress that while they can't always control change, they can always control their response, attitude, words and actions.

7. **Share Stanford University Psychologist Carol Dweck's insightful paradigm of the Growth Mindset vs. Fixed Mindset from her book** *Mindset: The New Psychology of Success.* She outlines how to be more focused on learning rather than looking good. Especially helpful for your naysayers and perfectionists.

8. Share how your team can support change:

   o If there's ambiguity and you need clarity, get it.

   o If you're concerned, express it constructively.

   o Don't be attached to the way things were.

   o Celebrate being uncomfortable— you're learning.

   o Learn from and lean on each other.

   o Trust the intentions of one another and the organization.

   o Expect it won't go perfectly and have empathy.

Bite-Size Step: On a semi-regular basis, when you're going through difficult changes or trying to learn a new framework or implement a new initiative, refer back to these underpinnings of change as a positive opportunity for growth, camaraderie and success.

C. Answer to Actualize Successful Significant Change

1. What change are you looking to implement?

   _____

   _____

2. Does it fulfill the mission, get you closer to the vision and in alignment with your values? How so? Why is this change important and meaningful?

   _____

   _____

   _____

   _____

3. Knowing it will require resources shifted from other priorities, is this change more important than what you've already committed to? As an organization, if we say yes to this, what are we saying no to? Triple check it's not a "flavor of the month" or a "shiny blinky."

_____

_____

4. If successful, what will this change do for the organization? If unsuccessful, what will be learned? What could be lost? How much of a risk is this _really_?

_____

_____

_____

_____

5. Speak to the heart and the mind will follow. Ask yourself, how would I describe the potential of what this change could bring if I was speaking to their hearts? (Story on page 131 of Culture Works is a good example.)

_____

_____

6. Be cognizant of timing. Is there value in waiting to incorporate this into the next set of strategic goals or does it need to be implemented now? Why? Is this really the best time? Will there ever be a good time?

_____

_____

7. What's the implementation plan? How will you measure progress? What are the milestones? Who's championing this effort? Who needs to be involved?

_____

_____

_____

_____

8. If possible and appropriate, before you launch into changing things up, take a few days. During that time, share with your team what you're thinking of implementing and ask for their input. Share:

   o Why this change is important.

   o What this change could do for the organization.

   o The options that were considered.

   o Why you think this is the best option.

   o Why now.

   o Based on what you know, the best case and worst case scenario.

   o The proposed implementation plan.

Then listen, intently. Take notes. Don't respond to concerns brought forth in the moment. Just listen and capture. Ask if anything else occurs to them in the next 48 hours to please let you know.

Then sleep on it. Review and assess their concerns. Are they valid? Have you addressed them? Should this be a pilot initiative instead? Send out a communication shortly after the 48 hours, detailing answers to their concerns. Communicate clearly if the project is green-lighted or is on temporary hold to evaluate and address concerns brought to the table.

Obstacle Obliterator: Always answer, **"What's in it for me?"** Share how a new change benefits their workplace experience. Perhaps they get to expand their contribution to the mission. Or it will create more ease, money and time in the long-term. Maybe it simply increases pride in being part of an organization who is innovative rather than status quo.

 Obstacle Obliterator: You cannot serve flavor of the month. Change has to be in alignment with the focused vision. Otherwise it's just "Squirrel!" Your team has to know changes have been thoughtfully evaluated. They have to know there is a method to the madness; that their efforts to shift towards a new "way" won't be squandered.

Mini-Mantra: Are we green and growing? Or ripe and rotten?

Checklist:

Check those action items you've complete.

A. _____ Evaluate Your Team's Change Reaction

B. _____ Implement a Change Upgrade

C. _____ Answer to Actualize Significant Successful Change

Results or Shifts

What's one meaningful positive shift, outcome or result you've noticed due to these efforts?

_____

_____

_____

Now go share your success with someone and celebrate.

Your Top Three Takeaways:

1. _____

2. _____

3. _____

Chapter 10: Create Culture Conducive to Change

Deep Dive Discussion Guide

Bring your leadership and/or management team together and discuss:

What was your #1 takeaway or insight from Chapter 10?

_____

_____

_____

What did you take on or try on with your team? How did that go? What was harder than you expected? What was easier than you expected?

_____

_____

_____

What's one meaningful positive shift, outcome or result that came out of your efforts? Pause to celebrate! If applicable, what are you going to do to maintain, sustain and continue to nurture that outcome?

_____

_____

_____

What support or help would you like to request from this team? Advice? Best practices? Lessons learned? Being held accountable for following through on a commitment or making a habit stick?

_____

_____

_____

Chapter 11

Expand Time and Boost Focus

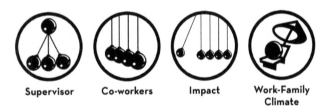

Supervisor   Co-workers   Impact   Work-Family Climate

"Tiiiiiiiiime, is on my side, yes it is."

—The Rolling Stones

An extraordinary workplace culture does not thrive when overwhelmed. Anxiety, dread, despair, paralysis, and procrastination flourish instead. Expand time and boost focus.

 Remember: You are not a victim of time. Time is the one equalizer. We all have 168 hours a week. We choose how we spend our time.

 Remember: Work takes place inside life. Work is a part of life. Every year, you give 2,000 hours of your life to your organization. So do each of your team members. Make their contribution worth it.

Obstacle Obliterator: If you have someone who's just "clocking in," express that work is a part of life. Have them realize they are contributing 2,000 hours of their life to this work in this year alone. Tell them not to waste it. Then revisit the purpose of your organization and have them really understand how their role is mission critical to the team's success.

A. Shift Your (and Your Team's) Relationship with Time

From the 18 options on the next few pages, circle the three time expanders that you will try on this next month:

 If what you choose requires blocking out time, do so now.

 Mini-Mantra: If what you choose requires creating a new habit or remembering, come up with a mini-mantra or write it down where you will read it every morning for 19 days.

1. **Give yourself more time,** more breathing room. For example, schedule 10 extra minutes before each appointment. If you like to snooze, instead of setting your alarm for the time you need to wake up, set the alarm for 15 minutes before you want to wake up and then again for the time you need to wake up.

2. **Change your language about time.** Name what you choose.
   Are these refrains common in your language, or that of your team?

   o "I don't have enough time."

   o "I have a zillion things to do."

   o "I'm swamped."

   o "So much to do, so little time."

   o "I never get anything done."

   Instead: "Between work, my kids' soccer, time with my beloved, rock climbing and painting the house, my life is really full. The truth is I choose it all. I wouldn't have it any other way."

    Remember: Your team is a reflection of you. If time poverty phrases fly out of your mouth with the greatest of ease, don't be surprised if they become team mantras as well as team scapegoats.

3. **Examine the purpose for each task on your list** and why it's important. If it's not, remove it and stop feeling guilty.

4. **Call due dates finish lines instead of deadlines.** Your team would rather feel like they're crossing a finish line, victory arms in the air, than a deadline, a word born of the boundary line that if crossed by a prisoner meant he would be shot dead.

5. **Manage your mood.** Remember, emotions are contagious. Listen to your favorite upbeat song on the way to work. Or if you're a "hangry" person, pack healthy snacks. Step outside and soak up some sunshine.

6. **Fill your energy bucket.** More energy gives you more rich time. Invest in your energy. Sleep, eat well, exercise. Take mental breaks. Do what brings you joy. Create and follow morning, afternoon and evening rituals that support your vitality. Know your peak productivity time.

7. **Choose progress over perfectionism.** We've all been there, paralyzed by minutiae. Attention to too much detail, fearful of not looking good. Ask, does it matter? To whom? Three years from now, will it matter? I appreciate excellence, but I appreciate darn good progress more.

8. **Stay present to slow down time.** In the *Art of Noticing*, Ellen Langer recommends actively noticing new things daily. Pause once a day. Look around. Notice, what's new about your workplace experience? Someone brought in a new kind of coffee. Bob got a new pair of blue suede shoes. That flickering overhead fluorescent light finally got fixed.

9. **Audit your time.** For one week, write down how you spend your time in 30-minute blocks. Notice...

   o What do you spend time on?

   o Where is your time well spent? What are "time-sucks?"

o When are you the most productive? Least productive?

o What are the circumstances that help you be your most productive?

o When is your down time?

o When do you procrastinate? Why?

10. **Break down your time and allot less.** Budget your calendar to figure out how you're going to spend your time for the week. Often we operate in hour-long chunks of time. But strategic bite-size tasks such as a phone call, initial research, or a check-in meeting with a co-worker can usually be accomplished in 20-minute blocks. Conversations and meetings expand to take the time allotted.

11. **Choose bite-size strategic steps.** When you're in overwhelm with "everything" you have to do, try the fog effect, where all you can see, and all you can you do, is the thing right in front of you. You can only accomplish one thing at a time. Everything else is outside of your periphery. Those things are not important now.

12. **Narrow your focus and write down your top three strategic tasks for tomorrow.** Every afternoon before you leave work, ask yourself what are the one to three things I could do tomorrow that would strategically and meaningfully move the ball forward? Two tools you can purchase online to help narrow your personal focus: the three month SELF Journal which aligns intention with action and Focus@will which provides music that neurologically helps you focus.

13. **Protect your plate.** If someone is asking you to add something to your plate and it's full, have a conversation about priorities. Clarify, what would you like me to take off to make room for this new item? Often, this conversation will be with yourself.

14. **Ask for what you need to be fully present.** If a team member interrupts you, rather than trying to do two things at once, ask your team member to give you five minutes or two hours until you can give them your full attention. Set your timer if need be. Before meeting with them, take a deep breath, feel your feet on the floor, and listen as if there were no one else in the world and nowhere else you have to be.

15. **Close your open door policy.** Hold office hours. Pick a consistent time that works for you and your team to touch base daily. Define what constitutes an appropriate interruption outside of those hours. Then hold them sacred and be present.

16. **Do a morning check-in and use a communication board.** Instead of having your employees come to you, go to your employees. Every morning have a 20 minute check-in with your team. On a communication board have these items to be reviewed:

o Current Projects

o Key Performance Metrics (Hitting? If not hitting, why?)

o New Ideas (to review, discuss and decide)

Almost every issue that arises during the day can wait until the following morning and goes up on the communication board. If it truly can't wait a day, have employees seek you out.

17. **Do the strategic work first.** Procrastination reigns as we embrace the dopamine hit of checking off easy items on the to-do list. Do you belong to the club of productive procrastinators? You may also be the type who, as you push aside strategic work, jumps in to help save the day, enjoying the immediate rush of validation. Either do the strategic work first or block out peak productivity time to accomplish it. Pause all interruptions and choose an environment where you're most productive.

 Remember: Lucille Ball and Ethel Mertz in the chocolate factory. Fix the conveyor belt.

Mini-Mantra: Do the work of the work. Make progress. Feel accomplished. Repeat.

18. **Decide What to Delegate**

   Grab a white board or piece of flip chart paper and try this simple exercise:

   o Write down a laundry list of everything you do and everything you're responsible for in a given month.

   o Circle in green everything you enjoy and that gives you energy.

   o Circle in orange everything you're really good at.

   o Circle in blue everything that's strategic, that will move your organization forward.

   o Circle in red everything ONLY YOU can do. Push yourself to answer this one strictly, meaning if you were out of the country, or got hit by a bus, could someone else do it?

   o Now take it in. What do you notice?

   o Some items might be circled multiple times. Keep these.

   o Some items have no circles. Delegate these items. Find someone who has this skill or train someone. Keep in mind this is a great growth opportunity for the person you entrust.

   o Prioritize the ones you are keeping.

   o If your list is still long, take the bottom three to five and give those away as well.

 Checklist:

Check those action items you've completed.

A. _____ One Time Expansion Effort

A. _____ Two Time Expansion Effort

A. _____ Three Time Expansion Effort

Results or Shifts

What's one meaningful positive shift, outcome or result you've noticed due to these efforts?

_____

_____

_____

Now go share your success with someone and celebrate.

Your Top Three Takeaways:

1. _____

2. _____

3. _____

Deep Dive Discussion Guide

Bring your leadership and/or management team together and discuss:

What was your #1 takeaway or insight from Chapter 11?

_____

_____

_____

What did you take on or try on with your team? How did that go? What was harder than you expected? What was easier than you expected?

_____

_____

_____

What's one meaningful positive shift, outcome or result that came out of your efforts? Pause to celebrate! If applicable, what are you going to do to maintain, sustain and continue to nurture that outcome?

_____

_____

_____

What support or help would you like to request from this team? Advice? Best practices? Lessons learned? Being held accountable for following through on a commitment or making a habit stick?

_____

_____

_____

Chapter 12

Make Meetings Meaningful

- Evaluate and Reduce Meeting Time
- Before You Call Another Meeting
- Improve Your Meetings
- Bonus: Apply Efficient Hand Gestures
- Empower Your People: Create A Decision Map
- Checklist, Results and Takeaways
- Deep Dive Discussion Guide

| Supervisor | Co-workers | Impact | Autonomy | Organizational Support |

"If you had to identify, in one word, the reason why the human race has not achieved, and never will achieve, its full potential, that word would be 'meetings.'"

—Dave Barry, author and humorist

 Remember: Have a meeting when you need to:

- Make a collaborative, democratic or consensus decision.
- Debate legitimate perspectives to get to a decision.
- Evaluate implementation on a proposed plan of action that requires participation by multiple parties.
- Address conflict.
- Conduct short, stand-up team coordination to quickly assess project progress and clarify next steps.

- Brainstorm solutions and then pick one.
- Share bad or sensitive news.

A. Evaluate and Reduce Meeting Time

Go back to a recent "typical" month in your calendar (not on vacation). List all of the meetings you had below. (Feel free to use the notes section at the back of the workbook if you have more than ten, according to Atlassian most office employees have 62 in a month.)

Value on a scale of 0–3:

- 3: Very valuable—definitely made rockin' progress
- 2: Good to get on the same page
- 1: Not the best use of my time
- 0: Really?

Meeting	Recurring	Number of people	Time	Highlights	Value
1.					
2.					
3.					
4.					
5.					
6.					
7.					
8.					
9.					
10.					

Now calculate:

- How many meetings did you have? _____
- How many of these meetings are recurring? _____
- What was the average length of those meetings? _____
- What was the total number of hours you spent in those meetings? _____
- Were you able to remember or point to the major highlights, outcomes or decisions from most of those meetings? _____
- What percentage of those meetings would you say fall into the following buckets:
    a. _____ Very valuable—definitely made rockin' progress
    b. _____ Good to get on the same page
    c. _____ Not the best use of my time
    d. _____ Really?

Ask your team to answer these same questions.

What do you notice? Which meetings are meaningful—why? Which ones are a time-suck—why?

_____

_____

_____

For those meetings that are a time-suck, do any of the following reasons apply? If so, write it next to that meeting.

    a. Lack of decisiveness

    b. Choking on two cents

    c. Collaboration becomes confused with consensus

    d. Cowardly consensus

    e. Poor facilitation

    f. Lack of a plan of action and follow through

    g. Sabotage and lack of in-the-room honesty

    h. Used only to inform

    i. Other _____

(Applying solutions is coming up in Exercise C on page 105.)

Remember: Reduce meeting creep. There's a tendency by teams to create a recurring meeting in an effort to feel like progress will inherently be built into the future. The intentions are good, however it's lazy planning that can often result in organizational procrastination.

Looking back at your list of meetings, where are there opportunities to:

• Reduce the frequency of a meeting?

• Reduce the length of a meeting?

• Reduce the number of people at a meeting?

If so, go do that now.

How many hours of meeting time was your entire team able to reduce in a month? _____
Focus 75 percent of this time towards strategic progress, production and execution. Leave the other 25 percent for breathing room, thinking room.

Obstacle Obliterator: If you find everything feels like meeting by committee, don't forget when to use collaboration and when not to use it, as outlined on pages 153 and 154 of *Culture Works*.

B. Before You Call Another Meeting

Answer the Dynamic Decision Dozen (especially if your culture suffers from chronically slow decision-making, or paralysis in choosing the right option).

1. Is there a decision to be made? (If not, don't have a meeting.) _____

    Exceptions: If you need to create an implementation plan, address conflict, share hard news, or conduct a "Cadence of Accountability" check-in.

2. What is the decision that needs to be made? Clearly define it.

   Decision to be made _____

   _____

3. Can this be decided with one other person? _____

4. Who *must* be involved?

   _____

   _____

5. Who will make the decision? _____

   o Authoritative—I'm making the decision.*

   o Collaborative—I'm looking for help to think this through, but I will ultimately make the decision.

   o Democratic—We'll put this to a vote, and the solution with the most votes wins.

   o Consensus—We all have to agree. (Use consensus sparingly. While it's excellent for garnering buy-in, it's very time-intensive and can lead to groupthink.)

   o Delegate—You decide without me.*

   *does not require a meeting

6. What type of decision needs to be made—yes/no or choosing the best option?

   _____

   _____

7. What criteria/boundaries does the decision need to take into consideration—budget, finish line, people power available, customers?

   _____

   _____

8. Which of these criteria are non-negotiable vs. like to have?

   _____

   _____

9. Is this decision more important than following through on our current commitments? What will we gain?

   _____

   _____

10. What will be lost or what will we regret if we just sit on this decision?

   _____

   _____

11. How urgent is the decision? What is the finish line for the decision?

   _____

   _____

12. What does the data say? What does my gut say?

   _____

   _____

C. Improve Your Meetings

Name three key meetings that are not meeting their full potential. Now look at the seven potential solutions outlined below and select one for each meeting to try on to make these meetings more meaningful.

Meeting:

1. _____

2. _____

3. _____

Solution:

1. _____

2. _____

3. _____

1. **Regularly implement the Dynamic Decision Dozen before calling a meeting.**

2. **Create cultural context and expectations for meetings.** Negative cultural underpinnings can undermine every effort to have an effective meeting. Look at the commitments below. Circle the five that would best address some of the meeting challenges at hand. Bring these to your next meeting. Ask the team to commit. Make sure to keep these top of mind by reading them once a month at the start of a meeting.

Meeting commitments:

o Be on time—this honors all of those involved.

o Read *and digest* supporting documentation prior to the meeting. Don't just skim.

o Be curious and fully present. Listen and contribute.

o Be open to the idea the meeting will unearth better ideas and solutions than you expect.

o Say what is. Express your concerns and questions IN the meeting, not after.

o Offer kind, candid, concise and constructive communication.

o Be committed to reaching an outcome that is best for the organization.

o Be solution and progress oriented. If it's 85 percent correct and there's no mission critical concerns, back the decision. The decision doesn't have to be perfect and nitpicking or micromanaging the details is exhausting and unproductive.Do NOT bully, manipulate, ramble, blame, stall or attack.

o Acknowledge decisions are adjustable as new information is provided.

o Only commit to action items and timelines you will follow through on.

o Leave aligned. Once the decision is made, support it.

o Don't be political.

"Politics is when people choose their words and actions based on how they want others to react rather than based on what they really think."

—Patrick Lencioni

3. **Designate a facilitator.** If you anticipate the meeting going longer than 30 minutes and including more than four people, have someone designated as the facilitator. Ideally this person is not the meeting host or decision maker who is attached to the outcome, but rather someone who can:

   o Keep everyone on track and focused.

   o Pause those who dominate the conversation.

   o Bring to the table those who are quieter. (Use a round robin approach to hear from introverts.)

   o Know when to allow the discussion to flow.

   o Bring conflict safely to the surface.

   o Momentarily take off the facilitator hat and contribute to the discussion.

   o Hold the group accountable for accomplishing the purpose of the meeting.

   o Call timing for the decision.

   o End the meeting on time.

4. **Add a Parking Lot.** Have a flip chart to jot tangents, digressions and detours that are captured but do not need to be considered right now. This acknowledges to your colleagues, in black and white for all to see, that their contribution was heard and won't be forgotten. It also communicates that while possibly important, this topic is not critical for this discussion and can be addressed in another forum. For virtual teams, consider using your IM window and note PL (Parking Lot) prior to the item.

5. **Focus on collaboration NOT consensus.** The purpose of most meetings is to choose the best option for moving forward, not to have everyone agree. However, many groups avoid conflict by seeking consensus. Critical evaluation of alternative ideas or viewpoints gets neglected, resulting in groupthink. There should be one person who is responsible for evaluating all of the input, feedback, questions, and concerns and making the final call. This person should state why they chose the option at hand and acknowledge the concerns voiced about this selection. This communicates to those who wouldn't have chosen this option their input was both heard and considered.

6. **Make real progress.** Whenever possible, conclude with a decision. Remember, the second best solution implemented is better than the best solution not implemented. If a decision needs more research, evaluation or time to marinate, nail down how many days are needed and schedule a decision finish line meeting.

7. **Capture, share and hold one another accountable for critical outcomes and commitments.** At the meeting, record the decision, the next steps and who is accomplishing which steps by when. *Confirm everyone in attendance agrees these are the outcomes of the meeting.* Designate someone to provide this summary to anyone who is impacted by the decision.

D. Bonus: Apply Efficient Hand Gestures

For one month, for all the meetings with more than five people, use hand gestures to communicate effectively, respectfully and efficiently:

● Thumbs up—I agree.

● Holding up a number of fingers to show where you are in line—I'd like to speak and recognize I'm after her.

● Making a wave or hilly movement—I was going to say something, but I'm good now.

● A "T" like timeout—we're going on a tangent.

- Thumb up, down, sideways—agree, disagree and block or neutral.
- Index finger twirl—wrap it up.

How'd it go?

_____

_____

E. Empower Your People, Create A Decision Map

A Decision Map is a one-page tool empowering people at every level to know which decisions they are responsible for and have control over and which ones they don't. (See the sample on page 149 of *Culture Works*.)

Questions to Create Your Decision Map

1. How are strategic decisions about the direction of your organization made?

_____

_____

_____

2. How are daily or weekly operational decisions made?

_____

_____

_____

3. When is there consistency? Inconsistency?

_____

_____

_____

4. Who makes what decisions? And with what permission? Who is responsible for which pieces? At the level of:

- Ownership
- Advisory Board
- CEO/Executive Director/Dean
- Leadership/Management Team/Administration
- Departmental Managers
- Supervisors
- Front Line Staff

_____

_____

_____

5. It's not realistic all decision points can be outlined on your map. How do you want people to respond when unexpected questions arise?

_____

_____

_____

Your Decision Map:

_____ Decisions

☐ _____

☐ _____

☐ _____

_____ Decisions

☐ _____

☐ _____

☐ _____

_____ Decisions

☐ _____

☐ _____

☐ _____

_____ Decisions

☐ _____

☐ _____

☐ _____

_____ Decisions

☐ _____

☐ _____

☐ _____

Checklist:

Check those action items you've completed.

A. _____ Evaluate and Reduce Meeting Time

B. _____ Before You Call a Meeting

C. _____ Improve Your Meetings

D. _____ Bonus: Apply Efficient Hand Gestures

E. _____ Empower Your People: Create A Decision Map

Results or Shifts

What's one meaningful positive shift, outcome or result you've noticed due to these efforts?

_____

_____

_____

Now go share your success with someone and celebrate.

Your Top Three Takeaways:

1. _____

2. _____

3. _____

Deep Dive Discussion Guide

Bring your leadership and/or management team together and discuss:

What was your #1 takeaway or insight from Chapter 12?

_____

_____

_____

What did you take on or try on with your team? How did that go? What was harder than you expected? What was easier than you expected?

_____

_____

_____

What's one meaningful positive shift, outcome or result that came out of your efforts? Pause to celebrate! If applicable, what are you going to do to maintain, sustain and continue to nurture that outcome?

_____

_____

_____

What support or help would you like to request from this team? Advice? Best practices? Lessons learned? Being held accountable for following through on a commitment or making a habit stick?

_____

_____

_____

Chapter 13

Implement Meaningful Performance Reviews

- Check Your Review Process for Best Practices

- Try The Duo-Review

- Develop Your Own Character and Competency Review

- Implement The High Five

- Checklist, Results and Takeaways

- Deep Dive Discussion Guide

Supervisor

Meaning/ Job Fit

Autonomy

Impact

Organizational Support

"An ounce of performance is worth pounds of promises."

—Mae West, actress, singer and provocateur

A. Check Your Review Process for Best Practices:

First, how well do you think your current review process works? Does it need to be upgraded or transformed?

_____

_____

_____

Then answer yes or no:

1. Do you hold the review in a neutral space? _____

2. Is your review form short and simple? _____

3. Do you conduct reviews when you say you will conduct them? _____

4. Do you talk about compensation **separate** from the review? _____

5. If you use scales, are they meaningful? _____

6. Do you address ugly issues in a timely fashion rather than waiting until a review? _____

7. Do you speak directly to overarching concerns? _____

8. Do you appreciate those efforts and behaviors you want to encourage? _____

9. Do you provide specific examples in both areas where they struggle and where they are having success? _____

10. Are you fully present when participating in a review? _____

Obstacle Obliterator: If your review process is working quite well and you were able to answer yes to all of the above, consider stopping here and putting your efforts elsewhere.

If you weren't able to answer yes to all of the above, what three bite-size steps will you take to improve your process?

1. _____

2. _____

3. _____

Implement The Triad which consists of the Duo-Review, the Character and Competency Review and the High Five. I recommend conducting all three of these within a year, with a rotation of one every four months.

B. Try on the Duo-Review

Both the manager and the team member should fill out the Duo-Review form (following page) prior to meeting.

At the meeting:

- Share what you appreciate about one another.

- Share up to three areas where the other person could improve or grow.

- Tell one another what you heard on both counts.

- Appreciate thoughtfulness and candor.

- Ask questions to uncover what specific shifts may be needed.

- Review progress on quarterly goals.

- Speak to what each of you is committed to in the next six months to both expand what's working and improve in the suggested areas.

Duo Review Form

Today's Date: _____   Manager Name: _____

Team Member Name: _____

Purpose and Intention: to learn from one another what you appreciate and what you can improve upon in order to create a better working relationship and more success in the workplace.

- Both the manager and team member should have a copy to fill out
- 40 minutes of scheduled **uninterrupted** time in a quiet space
- Bring a copy of the last review

A. **Appreciation—what's working**

　1. What the Manager appreciates about the Team Member:

　　_____

　　_____

　2. What the Team Member appreciates about the Manager:

　　_____

　　_____

B. **Opportunities for Improvement—what could work better**

　1. What the Team Member could improve on:

　　_____

　　_____

　2. What the Manager could improve on:

　　_____

　　_____

C. **Get real and get candid: Are there any major concerns/elephants in the room we're not addressing/talking about?**

　_____

　_____

D. **Look at progress on prior commitments from last review. On target? Behind? Change in priorities?**

　_____

　_____

E. **Three commitments/goals for next six months:**

　1. Manager:

　　_____

　　_____

　2. Team Member:

　　_____

　　_____

C. Develop Your Own Character and Competency Review

Your scorecard should measure two aspects - exemplification of the organization's values and position performance. (Refer to the example on page 162 and 163 of *Culture Works*.) The following couple of pages has a "blank" review you can use to create your own.

1. For your character section, simply pull over your values from your work on page 21, Flesh Out Your Values. Remember, this portion of the scorecard will stay the same across the organization.

2. For the competency section, simply pull over the position skills, knowledge and capacity you listed on pages 47 and 48, Clarify Character and Competency Expectations. Pull from this same work, three clear ways each capacity is demonstrated in the position. Remember, this portion of the scorecard will change for each position.

3. Then consider, are any of these performance criteria more important than others? If so, weigh these more heavily.

4. What percentage of the review will be weighted towards values and what percentage will be weighted towards performance?

   Values: _____%   Performance _____%

   Why this ratio of percentages? _____

   _____

5. What other areas of evaluation are important for your organization?

   _____

   _____

6. How will these be scored? (negative points, bonus points)

   _____

   _____

 Remember: Keep it short and simple.

Character and Competency Review Example

Date: _____ Employee Name: _____

Position: _____

Manager Name: _____

Hire Date: _____

A. Exhibits Our Culture and Values (____ total points possible, ____ percent)

Evaluate: Exemplary-3; Meeting Expectations-2; Needs Improvement-1; Unacceptable-0

1. Value _____   _____
    o _____
    o _____
    o _____

2. Value _____   _____
    o _____
    o _____
    o _____

3. Value _____   _____
    o _____
    o _____
    o _____

4. Value _____   _____
    o _____
    o _____
    o _____

5. Value _____   _____
    o _____
    o _____
    o _____

Total: _____

Divide total by ____ and multiply by ____

Comments:

_____

_____

_____

B. Position: _____

Skills/Knowledge/Capacity (____ total points possible, ____ percent)
Evaluate: Exemplary-3, Meeting Expectations-2, Needs Improvement-1, Unacceptable-0

1. Skill _____   ____
   - _____
   - _____
   - _____

2. Skill _____   ____
   - _____
   - _____
   - _____

3. Skill _____   ____
   - _____
   - _____
   - _____

4. Skill _____   ____
   - _____
   - _____
   - _____

                                                          Total: ____

                      Divide total by ____ and multiply by ____   ▨

C. Other: ▨
   - _____
   - _____
   - _____

D. Other: ▨
   - _____
   - _____
   - _____

                                   Total (add up all gray sections)   ▨

Comments:

_____

_____

_____

Now test your scorecard. Run several employees in different positions through, including high, medium and low performers.

Name of Employee	Score
_____	_____
_____	_____
_____	_____
_____	_____
_____	_____
_____	_____
_____	_____
_____	_____

Do the scores accurately reflect the difference between them? Or do you need to adjust?

 Once adjusted, go forth and implement! Schedule one-on-ones in your calendar now. *Protect this time.*

D. Implement The High Five

Once a year, have *every* employee, leadership included, select five co-workers from whom they think feedback would be the most valuable. It is then the employee's responsibility to set up 15-minute one-on-ones with each of these five co-workers. The employee asks the following questions:

What is the one thing:

1. You appreciate most about me as a co-worker?

2. I could do to be a better co-worker?

3. You think I rock at in my position?

4. I could do (or learn) to be better at my job?

5. I could do to help you be successful?

The employee can then directly ask for clarity, through **examples** as well as **suggestions.** This helps the person learn not only *what* to improve, but *how*. Because everyone participates in this process, everyone is more committed to being both humble and open to receiving input as well as courageous and kind in their feedback. The employee brings the feedback, insights and suggestions they received to a dialogue with their manager to talk through next steps.

 To make this process successful, train your team on the Five Success Factors of the giver and the receiver:

As the Feedback Giver:

1. **Show up on time.**

2. **Show up as a stand for the individual's success.** Your intentions will make all the difference in how your feedback is perceived and received.

3. **Be kind, candid and constructive.** Don't couch your communication. Don't be harsh.

4. **Don't phone it in.** Say something meaningful. Take time beforehand to think through what you want to convey. Come prepared with examples and suggestions.

5. **Start off with a humble qualifying statement.**

   ○ From my perspective...

   ○ In my experience working with you...

   ○ I may be missing something, however it would seem...

As a Feedback Receiver:

1. **Trust the givers' intentions.** They are there to help you be the best you can be—not to criticize or judge.

2. **Be curious, not defensive.** Stay present and seek to understand. Ask questions. (Sometimes you just need to take it in and sleep on it.)

3. **Be thankful for all suggestions.** Appreciate the courage it took for the other person to share their perspective and be straight with you.

4. **You don't have to take "on" all suggestions.** They may not all be accurate. Those that are repeated hold more weight.

5. **Lastly, don't get stuck in your head!** Instead make progress.

   How'd it go? What did you learn? What did your team learn?

   _____

   _____

   _____

 Checklist:

Check those action items you've completed.

A. _____ Check Your Review Process for Best Practices

B. _____ Try The Duo-Review

C. _____ Develop Your Own Character and Competency Review

D. _____ Implement The High Five

 Results or Shifts

What's one meaningful positive shift, outcome or result you've noticed due to these efforts?

_____

_____

_____

 Now go share your success with someone and celebrate.

💡 **Your Top Three Takeaways:**

1. _____

2. _____

3. _____

Deep Dive Discussion Guide

Bring your leadership and/or management team together and discuss:

What was your #1 takeaway or insight from Chapter 13?

_____

_____

_____

What did you take on or try on with your team? How did that go? What was harder than you expected? What was easier than you expected?

_____

_____

_____

What's one meaningful positive shift, outcome or result that came out of your efforts? Pause to celebrate! If applicable, what are you going to do to maintain, sustain and continue to nurture that outcome?

_____

_____

_____

What support or help would you like to request from this team? Advice? Best practices? Lessons learned? Being held accountable for following through on a commitment or making a habit stick?

_____

_____

_____

Chapter 14

Crack the Compensation Code

- Look at the Numbers

- Remedy Current Discrepancies

- Revisit How Compensation and Raises are Determined

- Evaluate Profit Sharing, Bonuses, Commissions and Incentives

- Mitigate Money Stories

- Optional: Provide a Clear Pathway to Earn More

- Optional: Define Bands to Value Your Best Producers

- Checklist, Results and Takeaways

- Deep Dive Discussion Guide

Supervisor

Co-workers

Organizational Support

Organizational Fit

"Price is what you pay. Value is what you get."

—Warren Buffett, investor and business magnate

A. Look at the Numbers

How much are you paying your people? Fill out the first three columns below. Pull the Character and Competency numbers from page 48. If you have their Character and Competency scorecard number from page 117, include that too.

Initials	Position	Pay	C&C Numbers
1. ____			
2. ____			
3. ____			
4. ____			
5. ____			
6. ____			
7. ____			
8. ____			

Now evaluate:

- When you compare, do those you pay more provide a bigger return on investment to the organization?

- Who is overpaid?

- Who is underpaid?

- Why are some people overpaid and others underpaid?

- Are your trust biases at play (from page 58)?

- Did you give someone an undeserved raise?

- Are you compensating for tenure rather than performance?

- Are you compensating more for expertise rather than execution?

- Does someone deserve a raise, but the organization needs to wait to be more financially stable?

- Where are your biggest discrepancies?

B. Remedy Current Discrepancies

This may include:

- Communicating to those who are overpaid that they will not be receiving additional raises until X performance is met, not because they aren't performing well, but because they are overpaid in comparison to their colleagues. It's a fairness issue. Have this conversation long before compensation conversations are due.

- Give raises to those who are underpaid now, rather than waiting until compensation conversations occur.

- If the organization isn't financially stable, communicate to those who are underpaid that when finances improve, you will adjust their pay.

Remedy the three biggest discrepancies by taking action this week. Who do you need to talk to to get the ball rolling?

1. _____

2. _____

3. _____

When will you meet with them? Block out time in your calendar now.

C. Revisit How Compensation and Raises are Determined

First, determine the range you're willing to pay for each position, rather than for a specific employee.

- What value does this position bring to the organization?
- How hard is it to find employees with these skills in the marketplace?
- What wage would be competitive in our marketplace?
- What wage can we afford when evaluating cost and profitability?
- What wage would reflect our values?
- Based on this information, what is the compensation range for this position?

Position Number 1 _____   Range _____

_____

_____

_____

Position Number 2 _____   Range _____

_____

_____

_____

Position Number 3 _____   Range _____

_____

_____

Second, look at each individual on your team:

- What is the value of the specific expertise, skills and relationships this individual brings to the organization?

- How productive is this individual?

- How well does this person exemplify the values of our organization? How much do they contribute to creating an extraordinary workplace culture?

- Has this employee increased their value to the organization by being more versatile, producing more revenue, reducing costs or producing better results?

Name of Employee	Specific Added Value
1. _____	_____
2. _____	_____
3. _____	_____
4. _____	_____
5. _____	_____
6. _____	_____
7. _____	_____
8. _____	_____

Obstacle Obliterator: What about seniority? Compensation packages should reflect performance, versatility and contribution rather than tenure. Honor loyalty and years of service through anniversary celebrations. Consider providing a universal gift for each year of service.

Obstacle Obliterator: The organization has to be financially healthy before doling out raises. When sharing the financials or the strategic plan, define what it means for the organization to be financially healthy. Clarify the revenue and profit numbers that have to be achieved before raises are given.

Obstacle Obliterator: Whatever you do, don't discourage employees from sharing their pay with one another. It suggests you have something to hide or that the system is not fair. Your employees will talk to one another. By trying to suppress those conversations you undermine your culture.

Remember: There are many creative ways to put together a compensation package. Consider all of the monetary, non-monetary, direct and indirect options on pages 175–176 of *Culture Works*.

D. Evaluate Your Current Profit Sharing, Bonuses, Commissions and Incentives

What do you provide regarding profit sharing, bonuses, non-sales commissions or incentives?

_____

_____

_____

What is your intention behind each of these efforts?

_____

_____

_____

Is your intention fulfilled? In essence, does this additional compensation accomplish what you had hoped? For example, appreciation, recognition, motivation or better performance? Or has it led to tension, broken promises, frustration or entitlement?

_____

_____

If it does accomplish what you had hoped, high five and keep on keepin' on.

However, if it wreaks havoc, apologize to your team and end this additional compensation. Explain how you had good intentions but that the outcome has been the opposite of what you had hoped. Consider leaning on the apology style outlined in "Wipe the Slate Clean" on page 85 of *Culture Works*.

 Remember: First, a financially healthy organization that can cover its payroll with ease, pay its vendors on time, has low to no debt, is able to invest in small niceties and has six months of expenses in the bank is more important to your culture than the short-term morale bump of profit sharing, bonuses, commissions and incentives.

Second, if people are paid well and fairly, and you have an extraordinary workplace culture, they don't need carrots. They will work hard for you because they care and they know you care.

Third, do not try to fix your culture challenges by throwing money at your team. It doesn't work. The elephants will still be there tomorrow, wearing a new jewel-encrusted tiara.

 Remember: If you're going to do bonuses, have them be unexpected and follow my recommendations on page 178 of *Culture Works*.

 Remember: Don't use perks to improve morale. Perks are great when they're just that—perks. Not mood manipulators.

E. Mitigate Money Stories

 Remember: Money is emotional. By association, compensation is emotional.

Every individual has a money story through which they filter their compensation.

Here are just a few common money filters:

- Money is the root of all evil.
- Money doesn't grow on trees.
- The best things in life are free.

- I can't hold on to money.
- There's never enough money.
- To want money is greedy.
- There's more where that came from.

If an employee understands their default money framework, it allows them to actively choose a different one. Especially if they take compensation as a concrete measurement of their worth. While you can't control these stories, under the umbrella of career development and financial literacy, you can suggest your team work through the questions below to create self-awareness.

First though, answer them for yourself:

1. What was your childhood experience of money? How did your parents handle money? What did they tell you about money? What was modeled for you? What money messages did you receive?

    _____

    _____

    _____

2. What are your beliefs and thoughts about money? What do you assume about people who have money? What do you assume about people who don't? What do you believe about your current financial situation?

    _____

    _____

    _____

3. What words do you associate with money? What do you say to your kids or to your friends about money? What advice do you give?

    _____

    _____

    _____

4. What are your habits around money?

    _____

    _____

    _____

5. Of these beliefs, words and habits, which serve you? Which don't?

    _____

    _____

    _____

6. How do you define financial freedom?

    _____

    _____

    _____

Remember: Psychological compensation can be as important as monetary compensation. Flexibility, alignment of values, appreciation, daily joy and humor, and camaraderie figure heavily into how an employee determines the value of working for you.

Remember: If you commonly have employees asking for a raise who haven't done anything to earn it, or who just recently received a raise, they may be telling you the psychological compensation isn't sufficient. If someone is not happy with the culture, it doesn't matter how much you pay. It won't be worth it. It won't be enough. This will become obvious when they leave even after you give them an unreasonable raise.

Obstacle Obliterator: Avoid extortion and support those who want to leave. Create a new cultural norm by both requesting and making it safe for employees to communicate that they are unhappy *prior* to looking for other work. If they give you this courtesy, support and encourage them in finding their next opportunity. In return, you'll receive support completing key work projects and training their replacement.

F. Optional: Provide a Clear Pathway to Earn More

If this model applies, compensate for value and versatility. Pay for learning *and applying* skills that bring value to the organization. We all have one person on our team who can pinch hit in multiple positions. They are your Swiss Army knife. Pay them as such. With this in mind, consider your list of ideal skills. Then provide them a clear pathway to earn more pay based on advancing their skills set, versatility and value. (Refer to the example on pages 170 and 171 of *Culture Works*.) Make sure to specify what constitutes demonstration, application and integration of a skill. As always, clarify the role character and values exemplification play in earning a bump in pay.

	Skill	Pay Bump	Skill	Pay Bump
Position 1				
	_____	_____	_____	_____
	_____	_____	_____	_____
	_____	_____	_____	_____
Position 2				
	_____	_____	_____	_____
	_____	_____	_____	_____
	_____	_____	_____	_____
Position 3				
	_____	_____	_____	_____
	_____	_____	_____	_____
	_____	_____	_____	_____

G. Optional: Define Bands to Value Your Best Producers

Define the range between the top pay and the bottom pay of each position. The space between is the bandwidth. What's key is to have the bottom pay of the next level be lower than the top pay of the prior position. Those looking for a promotion need to understand that initially they would make less money because their contribution to the organization in the new position is less. This also tells those remaining in the position that you value their mastery and expertise. Only those who are genuinely interested in the work of the open position—and the long-term earning potential—should apply.

Plug in your positions and your dollar values:

Position One	Position Two	Position Three	Position Four
			Top Pay $75K
		Top Pay $65K	
			Bottom Pay $61K
	Top Pay $55K		
		Bottom Pay $51K	
Top Pay $45K			
	Bottom Pay $41K		
Bottom Pay $35K			

These bands should be transparent to your team. This helps them understand the ceiling for each position. Using the clear pathway defined in Exercise B, define the skills to reach excellence for each band.

 ## Checklist:

Check those action items you've completed.

A. _____ Look at the Numbers

B. _____ Remedy Current Discrepancies

C. _____ Revisit How Compensation and Raises are Determined

D. _____ Evaluate Profit Sharing, Bonuses, Commissions and Incentives

E. _____ Mitigate Money Stories

F. _____ Optional: Provide a Clear Pathway to Earn More

G. _____ Optional: Define Bands to Value Your Best Producers

 ## Results or Shifts

What's one meaningful positive shift, outcome or result you've noticed due to these efforts?

_____

_____

_____

 Now go share your success with someone and celebrate.

Your Top Three Takeaways:

1. _____

2. _____

3. _____

Deep Dive Discussion Guide

Bring your leadership and/or management team together and discuss:

What was your #1 takeaway or insight from Chapter 14?

_____

_____

_____

What did you take on or try on with your team? How did that go? What was harder than you expected? What was easier than you expected?

_____

_____

_____

What's one meaningful positive shift, outcome or result that came out of your efforts? Pause to celebrate! If applicable, what are you going to do to maintain, sustain and continue to nurture that outcome?

_____

_____

_____

What support or help would you like to request from this team? Advice? Best practices? Lessons learned? Being held accountable for following through on a commitment or making a habit stick?

_____

_____

_____

Notes